Alternative Futures

Alberta's Boreal Forest
at the Crossroads

Richard R. Schneider

National Library of Canada Cataloguing in Publication Data

Schneider, Richard R. (Richard Roland), 1959-
    Alternative futures : Alberta's boreal forest at the crossroads /
Richard R. Schneider.

    Copublished by: Alberta Centre for Boreal Research
    Includes bibliographical references.
    ISBN 0-9696134-4-X

    1. Forest policy—Alberta. 2. Forests and forestry—Alberta,
Northern. 3. Taiga ecology—Alberta, Northern. 4. Forest
management—Alberta. I. Federation of Alberta Naturalists. II. Alberta
Centre for Boreal Research. III. Title.
SD568.A5S36 2002   333.75'097123   C2002-911134-X

Published by:
    The Federation of Alberta Naturalists
    11759 - Groat Road
    Edmonton, Alberta, T5M 3K6
    www.fanweb.ca
        and
    The Alberta Centre for Boreal Research
    P.O. Box 52031
    8210 - 109 St.
    Edmonton, Alberta
    T6G 2T5
    www.borealcentre.ca

Financial assistance for development and printing provided by:
    Alberta Ecotrust Foundation (www.albertaecotrust.com)
    Canadian Boreal Trust
    Canadian Parks and Wilderness Society - Edmonton Chapter (www.cpaws-edmonton.org)
    Federation of Alberta Naturalists (www.fanweb.ca)
    TD Friends of the Environment Foundation (www.td.com/fef)

Cover photo: Cleve Wershler
Printed in Canada by Friesens
Printed on Reincarnation Matte paper (100% recycled, 50% post-consumer waste, processed
chlorine-free)

To Hilde and Fred, for starting me on this path,
To my dearest Alina, for all her love and encouragement, and
To Anika and Sasha, whose generation deserves to inherit a healthy forest.

Table of Contents

Acknowledgements

The origin of this book can be traced to the Ecosystem Management Working Group of the Alberta Forest Conservation Strategy. I thank the members of this group, Ron Anderson, Cheryl Bradley, Keith Branter, Diana Brierly, Sheri Dalton, Brian Harris, Darryl Hebert, Cam McGregor, Frank Oberle, and Brad Stelfox, for the insightful discussions we had on the application of Ecosystem Management to Alberta.

For the last two years I have been part of a research group called the Adaptive Management Experiment Team. The efforts of this group to devise practical scientifically-based management solutions to forest land-use issues in Alberta provided much of the intellectual foundation of this book. I thank Stan Boutin, Mark Boyce, Matt Carlson, Roger Creasey, Steve Cumming, Elston Dzus, Dan Farr, Lee Foote, Werner Kurz, Fiona Schmiegelow, Brad Stelfox, Mike Sullivan, and Shawn Wasel for their invaluable insights.

The support of the board of the Canadian Parks and Wilderness Society in Edmonton, and the broader conservation community in Alberta, has been vital to the success of this project. In particular, I thank Connie Boyce, Kim Dacyk, Dave Dodge, Judy Evans, Brett Purdy, Sam Gunsch, Peter Lee, George Newton, Irma Rowlands, Glen Semenchuk, Jill Sturdy, Richard Thomas, Cliff Wallis, Helene Walsh, and a long list of CPAWS volunteers for their many and varied contributions.

This book has benefited greatly from the feedback I have received from reviewers. I thank Cindy Chaisson, Steve Cumming, Susan Hannon, Steven Kennett, Marty Luckert, Ellen MacDonald, Monique Ross, Dave Schindler, Fiona Schmiegelow, Samantha Song, Brad Stelfox, Kevin Timoney, Marian Weber, and Bob Wynes for taking time out of their busy schedules to provide their comments and to assist the project in other ways.

Shawn Wasel and other members of the Al-Pac Environmental Services Team have greatly facilitated the project by providing data and photographs. I also thank the many other individuals that contributed data or photographs for the book; Dr. James Burns at the Provincial Museum of Alberta and Alina Schneider for copy-editing the manuscript; Carol Dragich for assisting with the cover design; and Mona Southron at Alberta Ecological Information Services for providing reprints. Financial assistance for the development and printing of the book was provided by Alberta Ecotrust Foundation, Canadian Boreal Trust, Canadian Parks and Wilderness Society – Edmonton, Federation of Alberta Naturalists, and TD Friends of the Environment Foundation.

Last, but not least, I would like to express my gratitude to Larissa and Vladimir Lurye, Hilde and Fred Schneider, and Alina Schneider for their support on the "home front" during the writing of this book.

Preface

Although the forests of Alberta are, for the most part, publicly owned, the public has had remarkably little access to information about these forests. Moreover, the information that does get widely disseminated comes from government and industry sources that generally convey the message that "all is well". In reality, the current system of forest management in Alberta is a relic of the 1950s, and is in serious need of repair.

To address the need for a reliable independent source of information on the boreal forest, the Canadian Parks and Wilderness Society – Edmonton Chapter initiated the Alberta Centre for Boreal Research in 1999, and I became its Executive Director. The Centre is a non-profit Society, registered in Alberta, and maintains a web site at: www.borealcentre.ca. This book represents the culmination of the Centre's first three years of work.

The book describes two alternative futures for Alberta's boreal forest. The first is the future forest under the existing system of management. My aim here is to provide readers with a clear understanding of what is happening in the forests of northern Alberta today, and what this will mean to the forests of tomorrow if no changes are made. The second half of the book describes an alternative future based on the implementation of ecological forest management. Here I provide a synthesis of the relevant scientific literature and describe how this new approach could be applied in Alberta.

From the outset, this book was designed to be accessible to a broad public audience, even though it draws heavily from the scientific and management literature. My job, as I have taken it, has been to pull all the pieces together and present the whole in a manner that is understandable to all. The dozen or so technical terms that I could not avoid using are defined in the glossary.

In addition to providing an overview of boreal issues, the book is also intended to serve as a gateway to further study. Factual information is thoroughly referenced, using material that is, for the most part, available through the Alberta library system or on the Internet. Most of the graphs and tables can be downloaded in Excel format from the Forest Watch Alberta web site (www.forestwatchalberta.ca).

To assure readers that the information being presented is accurate and reliable, references are supplied to the original sources of data. Most chapters of the book were also reviewed by one or two members of the Centre's scientific review board, comprised of academics with relevant experience (See the Centre's web site for more details). The reviewers were asked to identify errors of fact and omission.

Although the book is intended to provide a comprehensive guide to the boreal forest, some narrowing of the scope was required to keep the project manageable. For example, the spatial scope was limited to forests above 55 degrees latitude, even though some boreal forest extends south of this. To simplify the discussion of management options I excluded forests that are not on Crown lands. The whole issue of native rights and land claims, although integral to land-use planning in the North, was not addressed, mainly because I lack the expertise to do so. Finally, some specific issues, such as open pit oil sands mining, agricultural expansion, and global warming could not be given the attention they deserve within the time and resources available to this project.

I believe that an informed and motivated public is vital for the conservation of Alberta's northern forest. My hope is that by raising awareness of problems, and providing viable alternative approaches to management, this book will help swell the ranks of informed and motivated individuals and support their efforts to advance conservation in Alberta.

Part I
The Old Way

C. Truscott

1. Introduction

For many Albertans, the northern forest is synonymous with the concept of wilderness. It is a place for fishing and camping trips, where one might hear the call of a loon or the howl of a wolf. Perhaps, with a bit of luck, a chance encounter with a moose or a bear. Most importantly, the north is thought of as a place where nature prevails, in contrast to the southern plains that have largely been tamed by man.

Although loons and bears are still to be found, the face of the north is rapidly being transformed. Yesterday's wilderness is today's "resource". Each year, thousands of hectares of old-growth forest are replaced by clear-cuts, thousands of additional hectares of productive forest are converted to oil and gas wellsites, and tens of thousands of kilometres of new seismic lines, roads, and pipelines fragment the remaining forest landscape. Only the far northeast corner of the province is not being significantly affected, by virtue of the fact that petroleum deposits and commercial forest are largely absent there. By analogy, the current industrial complex and associated regulatory framework represent a freight train that is rapidly moving the forest down a new track. The question is, are we rolling in the right direction?

Given that most of the northern forest in Alberta is publicly owned, the desired future forest is defined by the values held by the citizens of Alberta. These values have been clearly articulated in the *Alberta Forest Conservation Strategy* (AFCS), the result of more than three years of dedicated effort by over 800 Albertans representing the full spectrum of forest stakeholders (AFCSSC, 1997). As expressed in the AFCS (AFCSSC, 1997: p. 3), the desired goal is:

> *To maintain and enhance, for the long term, the extent and health of forest ecosystems in Alberta for the sake of all living things locally, provincially, nationally and globally, while providing environmental, economic, recreational, social and cultural benefits for present and future generations.*

This statement includes several important concepts. First, it says that we are concerned with the state of the forest over the long-term. Second, it says that the forest should provide economic benefits, but these economic benefits do not have primacy over other benefits, nor are they to be derived at the expense of the health of the forest. Finally, the forest should continue to meet the needs of other species besides our own.

Although the provincial government accepted the vision, goal, and principles of the AFCS (AEP, 1998: p. 7), the system of forest management that is currently in place seems unlikely to achieve the objectives of the *Strategy*. In part, this is because there exists no plan for achieving those objectives. Broad policy statements and good intentions notwithstanding, current management continues to be focussed on maximizing economic returns over a short planning horizon. Ecological objectives, to the extent that they are addressed at all, are largely handled through local mitigation efforts. A long-term planning framework with clearly defined ecological objectives that integrates the activities of resource companies and places limits on cumulative industrial impacts is completely lacking. Finally, there is no system for effectively monitoring the changes in forest structure that are occurring, or determining their impact on forest wildlife, now and into the future.

Although it does not seem likely that the current system of forest management will achieve the future forest envisaged in the AFCS, this does not imply that the objectives of the *Strategy* cannot be realized. A viable alternative approach to forest management has been developed and refined over the past decade by researchers from around the world. Local research organizations, including the Sustainable Forest Management Network (headquartered at the University of Alberta) and the Alberta Research Council, have been important contributors to this field.

The new approach to management, usually referred to as Ecological Forest Management (EFM) or Ecosystem Management, emphasizes the maintenance of natural forest structures, patterns, and processes. This is accomplished through changes in planning and practices whereby industrial disturbances are made to approximate natural disturbances such as fire, to the greatest extent possible. In addition, the forest is carefully monitored for signs of unexpected changes, so that management plans can be adjusted prior to the development of serious problems. Plans are also adjusted in response to new scientific information as it becomes available. EFM is further characterized by a precautionary approach that includes the use of protected areas for risk management (among other roles). Finally, management decisions under EFM are made with public input and include a clear link to publicly defined values.

In Part I of this book I review the current system of forest management and provide a detailed description of the ongoing transformation of the forest. My focus is on northern Alberta, north of 55 degrees (Fig. 1.1). I begin, in this chapter and the next, with a description of the forest and the history of industrial development from 1900 to 2000. In Chapters 3 and 4 I take an in-depth look at the two most important industrial sectors in northern Alberta, forestry and petroleum, as they are today. I conclude Part I with a projection of the future forest under the current management regime and a summary of the deficiencies of the current regime relative to the goals defined in the AFCS.

In Part II of the book I outline an alternative approach to forest management, leading to an alternative future forest. This section is based on a synthesis of the recent scientific literature on EFM, in a form that is intended to be accessible to a non-technical audience. Chapter 6 is focussed on the natural disturbance model of forest harvesting, Chapter 7 reviews the role of protected areas in EFM, and Chapter 8 covers the special case of managing old-growth forest. In the final chapter I pull all the pieces together to describe what a workable system might look like and to provide some general conclusions. Although there can be no guarantees that EFM will achieve all of the objectives defined in the AFCS, there is little doubt that it stands a much higher probability of doing so than the current system.

Alberta's Boreal Forest

The forest of northern Alberta is part of the vast boreal forest that spans Canada and the globe (Fig. 1.2). South of the boreal forest is the aspen parkland forest, transitional between the boreal and grasslands. North of the boreal (beyond Alberta's border with the Northwest Territories) is the open forest of the Canadian Taiga.

As typical of boreal systems, the winters in northern Alberta are long and cold and the summers are short and cool. Precipitation is moderate but variable. In some years, extended hot and dry conditions lead to large fires that occasionally burn hundreds and even thousands of square kilometres of forest (in Chapter 6 I provide a detailed review of fire patterns in northern Alberta).

The surface features of northern Alberta are quite varied. The influence of the Rocky Mountains is evident in the foothills found in the southwestern quarter (Fig. 1.3). The rest of the region

Fig. 1.1. The scope of this book is northern Alberta, defined as the region north of 55 degrees latitude.

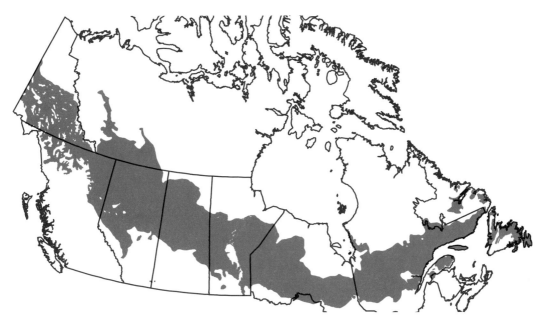

Fig. 1.2. Canada's boreal forest, as defined by the Canadian Forest Service. (Map: Forest Watch Alberta)

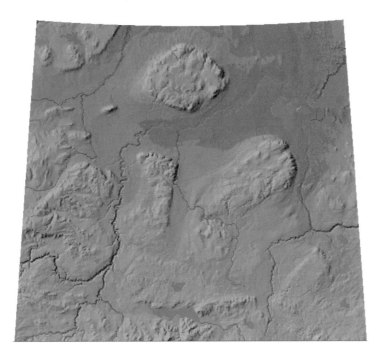

Fig. 1.3. Elevation map of northern Alberta. Higher elevations in brown; lower in green. (Map: Forest Watch Alberta)

consists of broad lowland plains and discontinuous hill systems. With the exception of the foothills and a small area of Shield in the northeast, the bedrock is buried beneath deep glacial deposits.

Upland forests are typified by a mosaic of pure and mixed stands of aspen and white spruce (Stelfox, 1995: 1; Fig. 1.4). Pure and mixed stands of black spruce and larch (on wetter sites), and jack pine (on drier and sandy sites) are also common (Stelfox, 1995: 2). Other common deciduous trees include balsam poplar and white birch. At higher elevations, pure stands of lodgepole pine, white spruce, black spruce, and subalpine fir are predominant. The mosaic of stand types characteristic of Alberta's boreal forest is the result of variability in local site conditions and cycles of disturbance and renewal (reviewed in Chapter 6).

Extensive wetlands are characteristic of the region. Peatlands, with open forests of black spruce and Labrador tea, are the dominant landform across approximately one-quarter of the area (Figs. 1.5, 1.6). Lakes are relatively rare, compared to other boreal systems. There are two major river systems in the region, the Peace and

Fig. 1.4. Examples of the boreal mixedwood forest typical of upland sites in northern Alberta. (Photos: D. Mussell, left; Al-Pac, right)

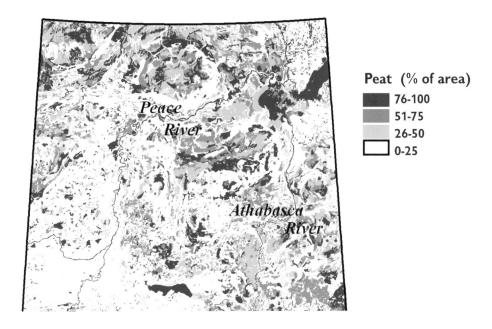

Fig. 1.5. Distribution of peatlands in northern Alberta. Source: Vitt et al., 1998.

Peat (% of area)
76-100
51-75
26-50
0-25

Fig. 1.6. Typical wetland in northern Alberta. (Photo: Canadian Parks and Wilderness Society)

Athabasca, which drain into the Peace-Athabasca delta in the northeast (Fig. 1.5). This delta, which is one of the world's largest inland freshwater deltas, drains into the Arctic ocean, primarily via the Slave River.

Because of variability in surface features, climate, and other attributes, Alberta's boreal forest is far from uniform. Regional differences exist and must be accounted for in any system of land use planning. To address this issue the provincial government developed a classification scheme that divides the province into a series of natural regions (AEP, 1994). Under this provincial scheme, Alberta's boreal forest is divided into three natural regions: the Boreal Forest proper, the Foothills, and the Shield (Fig. 1.7). The Boreal Forest Natural Region is in turn subdivided into six subregions, on the basis of vegetation, soils, and landforms (AEP, 1994).

7

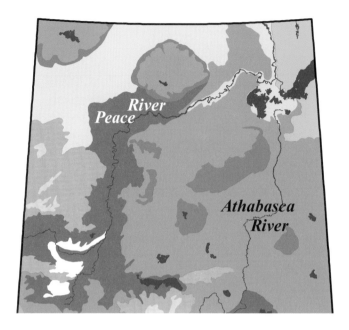

Fig. 1.7. The natural subregions of northern Alberta. (Map: Forest Watch Alberta)

Literature Cited

AEP (Alberta Environmental Protection). 1994. Natural Regions of Alberta. Alberta Environmental Protection, Edmonton, AB.

AEP (Alberta Environmental Protection). 1998. The Alberta forest legacy. Alberta Environmental Protection, Edmonton, AB. (Available at: www.gov.ab.ca/env/forests.html).

AFCSSC (Alberta Forest Conservation Strategy Steering Committee). 1997. Alberta forest conservation strategy. Alberta Environmental Protection, Edmonton, AB. (Available at: www.borealcentre.ca/reports/reports.html)

Stelfox, J. B. 1995. Relationships between stand age, stand structure, and biodiversity in aspen mixedwood forests in Alberta. Alberta Environmental Centre, Vegreville, AB. (Available at: www.borealcentre.ca/reports/reports.html)

Vitt, D. H., L. A. Halsey, M. N. Thormann, and T. Martin. 1998. Peatland inventory of Alberta. University of Alberta, Edmonton, AB.

Alberta Community Development

2. History of Industrial Development: 1900–2000

Northern Alberta in 1900

Although the settlement and transformation of southern Alberta was well underway by the late 1800s, northern Alberta at the turn of the 20th century remained in an essentially pristine state. The small human population that existed in the north at this time was still mostly native, and life continued to revolve around trapping, fishing, and hunting, as it had for more than a century (Wetherell and Kmet, 2000: 107). Major river corridors still served as the primary transportation routes, augmented by a trail system that was maintained by the Hudson's Bay Company (Stelfox and Wynes, 1999: 6-54).

Although the fur trade of the 19th century was not associated with significant structural changes to the boreal forest, increased rates of mortality from trapping and hunting with firearms did directly affect several species. In most cases, populations were able to recover once the rate of trapping declined after the 1930s (through regulation and reduced demand for wild fur). However, the hunting of wood bison to sup-

9

ply brigades and trading posts almost led to their extinction before conservation measures were enacted.

Wood bison are large animals that tend to herd together in open meadows, making them highly vulnerable to mass slaughter. By 1891 there were only a few hundred animals remaining, centred in the region that is now Wood Buffalo National Park (Carbyn et al., 1993: 18). The Dominion Government passed a law in 1893 to protect the remaining animals and in 1922 Wood Buffalo National Park was established to ensure their permanent viability (Gates et al., 1992: 145). Bison numbers did recover substantially; however, through management error in the late 1920s the wood bison were hybridized with plains bison and infected with tuberculosis and brucellosis (Gates et al., 1992: 146). Because of these problems the long-term future of wood bison in Alberta remains uncertain.

Settlement patterns

Several unique features of northern Alberta marked it for early development, relative to the northern regions of other provinces. These included the existence of large tracts of arable land along the Peace River (including several large open prairies), widespread deposits of oil, and the existence of a well established northern supply centre (Edmonton). Although these features were well known prior to 1900, several developments had to occur before large-scale settlement could proceed:

1. First Nations Treaty. Until Treaty 8 was signed with the First Nations chiefs in 1899, there existed no legal basis for the private ownership of land in the north.

2. Development of administrative and legal infrastructure. Prior to the onset of homesteading, the land had to be surveyed, First Nations reserves had to be designated, homesteading policies had to be defined, and local police detachments had to be established to enforce social order.

3. Development of Marquis wheat. Marquis wheat was a high-quality early-maturing variety of wheat introduced in 1910 that resolved concerns about northern Alberta's short growing season (Wetherell and Kmet, 2000: 130).

4. Settlement of the south. Demand for homesteads in the north became significant only after good-quality land in the south became scarce, after 1900 (Wetherell and Kmet, 2000: 129).

5. Establishment of railway links. A market economy for agricultural and other products could not be established until rail links were available for transporting goods to population centres in the south.

Progress on all fronts was rapid and by 1909 the first land office was opened and homesteaders began entering the north in large numbers (Stelfox and Wynes, 1999: 6-20). Most of the settlers were drawn by the prospect of farming; therefore, settlement was focussed almost exclusively on the arable land in the Peace River region. By 1931, the population of the south Peace River region had grown to almost 51,000 (Wetherell and Kmet, 2000: 243).

In 1939 the province moved to a system in which land capacity became the basis for land grants, in place of the haphazard homesteading system (Wetherell and Kmet, 2000: 255). A formal land classification scheme was implemented in 1948 that restricted agricultural settlement in the north to a defined area along the Peace River now known as the White Zone (Fig. 2.1). The remaining area, called the Green Zone, was deemed best-suited to non-agricultural use (though grazing reserves were still permitted). These land designations were not set in law and, therefore, remain subject to change at any time at the discretion of the Minister (Moen, 1990: 14).

After the Depression the population of the Peace River region grew steadily, at a rate similar to that of the province as a whole (Fig. 2.2). Farming continued to be a major driver of this growth; however, increasing need for support services

(e.g., education, medical care, administration) also resulted in the growth of local urban communities (Fig. 2.2). In the latter half of the century the expanding petroleum and forest industries became the main drivers of continued growth in the region (Stelfox and Wynes, 1999: 6-21).

In contrast to the rapid settlement of the Peace River region, settlement of northeast Alberta was very limited in the first half of the century — so much so that northeast and northwest Alberta began to function as two separate units. The west was farm country, which was economically and socially an extension of prairie settle-

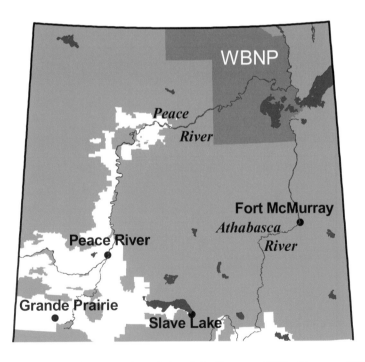

Fig. 2.1. Northern Alberta, showing the current boundaries of the Green and White Zones, and Wood Buffalo National Park (WBNP). (Map: Forest Watch Alberta)

ments to the south. The east was still primarily dependent on trapping, and continued to serve as a transportation corridor to the far north.

Rapid population growth did occur in the northeast after 1960, primarily because of the expansion of the petroleum industry (Fig. 2.3). Almost all of the growth occurred in Fort McMurray and surrounding area, which served as the primary support centre for the oil sands mines and other petroleum activities in the region.

As of 2000, the official population count in the northwest was 118,103, and 64,735 in the northeast (4.1 and 2.2 percent, respectively, of the total provincial population) (AMA, 2001). Most urban communities are in the northwest, including 13 towns with more than 1000 people (Figs. 2.4, 2.5a) (AMA, 2001). In the northeast only Fort McMurray and Slave Lake significantly ex-

ceed 1000 people, and they account for 83% of the permanent residents of the region (Fig. 2.5b). Fort Chipewyan, the third largest town in the northeast, has a population of approximately 1000.

Access Development

The transportation infrastructure that was initially developed in the north was closely linked to the needs of the agricultural community in the Peace River region. A railway link to from Edmonton to Grande Prairie was established in 1916. This was followed by regional rail links and the development of a local road network. By 1924, 140 km of roads were in place in the Peace River region (Wetherell and Kmet, 2000: 192). A road from Grande Prairie to Edmonton was completed in 1932, though it was not fully grav-

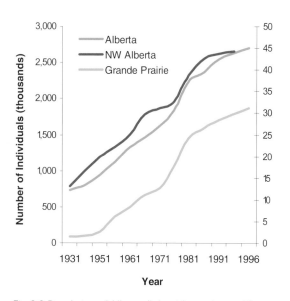

Fig. 2.2 Population of Alberta (left axis), northwest Alberta (north of 56 degrees; right axis), and Grande Prairie (right axis): 1931-1996. Sources: Stelfox and Wynes, 1999; GPCCD, 2001

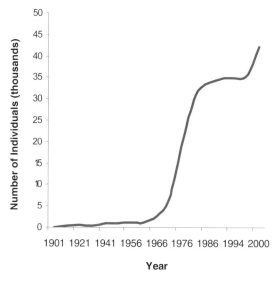

Fig. 2.3. Population of Fort McMurray: 1901-2000. Source: FMHS, 2001.

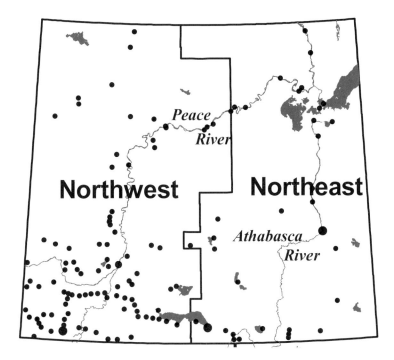

Fig. 2.4. Distribution of towns and hamlets in northern Alberta. Division into east and west is based on Municipal District boundaries. Southern boundary is 55 degrees latitude. (Map: Forest Watch Alberta)

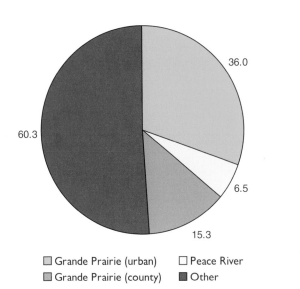

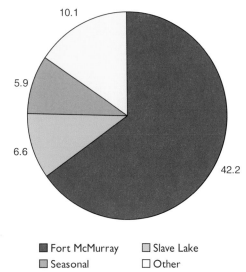

Fig. 2.5a. Distribution of population in northwest Alberta in 2000 (thousands). Source: AMA, 2001.

Fig. 2.5b. Distribution of population in northeast Alberta in 2000 (thousands). Source: AMA, 2001.

elled until after World War II (Wetherell and Kmet, 2000: 192).

In the east, a railway from Edmonton to Waterways, near Fort McMurray, was completed in 1922, which led to the emergence of Fort Mc-Murray as the new gateway to the north, in place of Athabasca. The Athabasca River continued to serve as the major transportation corridor north of Fort McMurray throughout the first half of the century. A highway to Fort McMurray was not completed until the 1960s.

The basic highway system established in the first half of the 20th century did not change substantially in later decades. Major routes were paved and secondary roads were improved and gravelled, primarily within the White Zone (Fig. 2.6). The major change that occurred during the latter half of the century was a profound increase in low-grade access to the forest. By 2000, access

routes developed by the petroleum and forest industries had permeated almost all of northern Alberta (Fig. 2.7). The only area that remains relatively inaccessible at present is land adjacent to Wood Buffalo National Park, which (not coincidentally) is the only part of Alberta not underlain with petroleum deposits (ERCB, 1992).

Agriculture

The early history of agriculture in northern Alberta is similar to the history of homesteading in the Peace River region, as previously described. Although most early farmers engaged in mixed farming to some degree, their primary focus was the production of grain crops. Consequently, the expansion of agriculture was coincident with the rapid clearing and cultivation of forested land (Fig. 2.8). After World War II the rate of forest

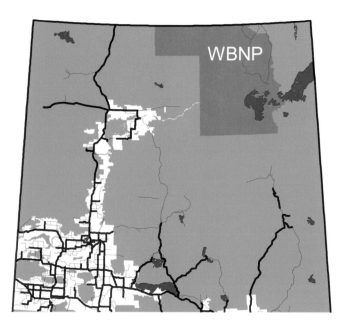

Fig. 2.6. Distribution of paved roads (black) and major gravelled roads (red) in northern Alberta, overlaid on the boundaries of the Green Zone and White Zone. (Map: Forest Watch Alberta)

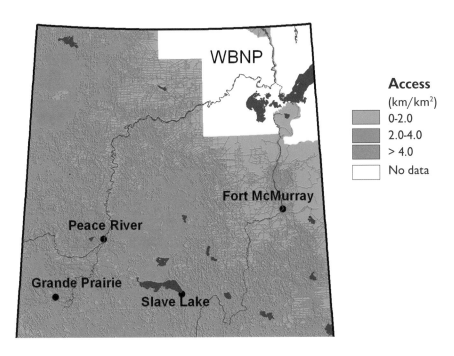

Fig. 2.7. Access density (km/km²) in northern Alberta in 2000. Seismic lines and trails were included in the analysis. (Map: M. Sawyer for Global Forest Watch Canada –methodology described in Smith and Lee, 2000: 105)

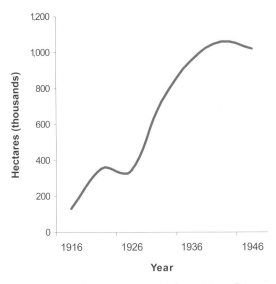

Fig. 2.8. Area of grain crops in the Peace River Country, 1906-1946. Source: Wetherall and Kmet, 2000: 262.

conversion accelerated, as higher incomes and increasing use of tractors permitted faster clearing (Wetherell and Kmet, 2000: 278).

Agriculture continued to dominate the economy of the Peace River region in the latter half of the century, and the conversion of forest to agricultural use continued as well. In the 1991 edition of Environment Canada's *State of Canada's Environment Report*, the Peace River region was described as "Canada's fastest-advancing agricultural frontier" (EC, 1991: 5-9). Between 1961 and 1986 the proportion of land converted to agricultural use in this region rose from 26.3% to 46.2% (EC, 1991: 5-9) (Fig. 2.9). The Environment Canada report (1991: 5-9) also concluded that much of the land that was converted to agricultural use was in fact best suited to for-

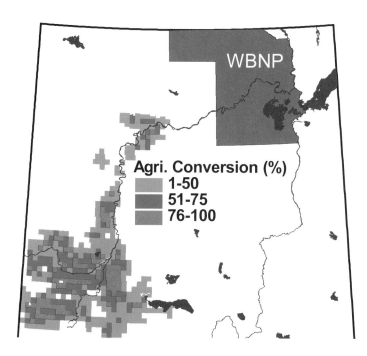

Fig. 2.9. Percent conversion of forest to agricultural use in the White Zone in 1996, by township. (Map: Forest Watch Alberta, based on Prairie Farm Rehabilitation Administration data)

estry and that the rapid rate of forest conversion threatened the sustainability of wildlife habitats in the region.

In addition to grain farming, northern Alberta also supports a significant livestock industry. This primarily involves various types of cattle operations, production of forage crops on private land, and grazing on public lands. As of 2001 there were 2817 grazing dispositions on public lands north of the North Saskatchewan River totalling 1.01 million ha (AAFRD, 2001).

Harvesting of Wildlife

The following sections deal with the commercial aspects of harvesting wildlife. It should be noted that in addition to direct effects on the species

being harvested, trappers, hunters, and anglers also exert significant influence on forest structure through their use of and demand for access. Once roads or seismic lines are constructed by resource companies, this group of users typically resists efforts to close or reclaim the new access routes. In addition, the continued use of trails and seismic lines by off-road vehicles and snowmobiles has been cited as a factor in delaying natural regeneration of these routes (Revel et al., 1984: 19).

Trapping

The rate of trapping initially increased after 1900 due to generally rising prices, improved access, and the influx of white settlers who engaged in trapping during the winter months. This increased rate of trapping resulted in a decline in furbearer populations (Wetherell and Kmet, 2000: 376). In response, the province began regulating harvests, eventually implementing a registered trapline system in 1939. Falling fur prices and increasing production of farm-raised fur also served to moderate trapping rates after the late 1920s (Wetherell and Kmet, 2000: 364).

In recent decades the demand for wild fur has declined significantly. There are currently approximately 2300 trappers in the province, though few of these rely on fur sales as their sole source of income (Stelfox and Wynes, 1999: 10-47; ASRD, 2001a). In 2000/2001 the total return from wild fur sales in Alberta was approximately $2.1 million (ASRD, 2001a). Most furbearer populations (Table 2.1) are now considered stable, with the exception of wolverine. Wolverine populations have declined in most regions of Alberta and the species is considered to be at risk of extinction if current trends continue (Peterson,

1997). In spite of these negative trends, and knowledge that wolverines reproduce slowly, trapping of this species continues to be permitted (37 caught in 2000) (ASRD, 2001b).

Hunting

Although the sale of wild meat was banned in 1922, sport hunting continues to be an important contributor to the northern economy. Commercial aspects include professional guiding and outfitting, and the provision of other support services (e.g., food, gas, lodging, equipment, etc.). Altogether, big game hunters contributed approximately $172 million to the provincial economy in 1996, much of which was expended in the north (McFarlane et al., 1998).

The sale of wildlife certificates (required by hunters to obtain a hunting licence) has significantly declined over the past two decades (ASRD, 2001c). In the past five years, sales have been at

Table 2.1. List of animals trapped and hunted in Alberta in 2001.

Species Trapped	Mammals Hunted	Birds Hunted
Badger	Bighorn Sheep	Mallard Duck
Beaver	Black Bear	Pheasant
Coyote	Cougar	Blue Grouse
Fisher	Coyote	Canada Goose
Lynx	Elk	Gray Partridge
Marten	Grizzly Bear	Merriam's Turkey
Mink	Moose	Ptarmigan
Muskrat	Mountain Goat	Ross's Goose
Otter	Mule Deer	Ruffed Grouse
Red Fox	Pronghorn Antelope	Sharp-tailed Grouse
Red Squirrel	White-tailed Deer	Snow Goose
Weasels	Wolf	Spruce Grouse
Wolf		Whitefronted Goose
Wolverine		

Source: SRD, 2001a; SRD,2001c.

their lowest level since these certificates came into use in 1964 (ASRD, 2001c). There has also been a long-term trend in the province to increased regulation, including limits on which animals can be taken, seasons, bag limits, and so on. These developments would suggest a declining risk to hunted populations. However, the dramatic increase in access in northern Alberta in recent decades presents a significant new risk factor. Increased access is of particular concern in light of continued poaching and sale of poached meat throughout the north. Furthermore, there are now few areas in the north that function as wildlife reserves, in which wildlife populations experience little or no hunting pressure.

Most hunted species in Alberta (Table 2.1) are currently considered to be relatively stable, with the exception of grizzly bears. Grizzlies are on the provincial "blue list", indicating that they may be at risk of extinction (AEP, 2000). In spite of this designation, the province continues to permit an annual grizzly hunt. Although few animals are actually killed, the hunt is completely contrary to efforts to maintain the viability of this species.

Even though moose populations are not considered to be at risk of extinction, concerns have been expressed by subsistence and recreational hunters about declining moose numbers (AEP, 1998a). Population surveys in northern Alberta have shown that the density of moose decreases with proximity to roads (Schneider and Wasel, 2000). In response, the province is proposing to "*move from a simple management system appropriate for a low human population and an unlimited moose supply to a more sophisticated management system appropriate for a larger and growing human population and greatly increased access to moose range.*" (AEP, 1998a).

Fishing

Commercial fishing became viable in northern Alberta only after rail links were established, making it possible to transport fish to southern markets in a fresh state. Once these rail links were in place the fishing industry expanded rapidly (Fig. 2.10), and with it a cycle of depletion of stocks and search for new unexploited lakes (Wetherell and Kmet, 2000: 339). Once the supply of new lakes and healthy fish stocks was exhausted, the commercial fishing industry in Alberta collapsed (Fig. 2.10). From a high of almost 8000 commercial operators in 1959, there remain today less than 1000 operators (SC, 1983; AEP, 1998b: 108). Lake whitefish and tullibee make up about 80% of the current commercial catch, with the remainder made up of northern pike, walleye, and incidental catches (AEP, 1998b: 108b). The total commercial catch in Alberta in 1997 was

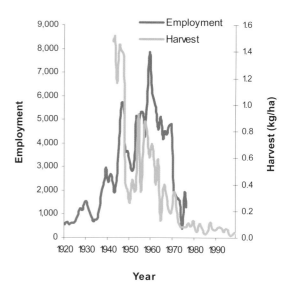

Fig. 2.10. Number of commercial fishing operators in Alberta and rate of commercial walleye harvest: 1920-1998. Sources: SC, 1983 and AB Environment records.

worth $2.8 million (Stelfox and Wynes, 1999: 10-41).

In the latter half of the 20th century, sport fishing overtook commercial fishing as the dominant form of fish harvesting. The number of sport anglers increased steadily until the early 1980s, and then declined by about 35% in the latter half of that decade (ASRD, 2001d). Since the early 1990s the number of anglers has been relatively stable. It is estimated that about 350,000 people fished in 2000 (ASRD, 2001d) and that approximately 80% of the total fish catch in Alberta now goes to sport anglers (AEP, 1998b: 108). Yellow perch, northern pike, walleye, and trout species account for 95% of the sport catch. Approximately $349 million were spent on sport fishing in Alberta in 1994, including expenditures on gear (Stelfox and Wynes, 1999: 10-33).

Even though sport fishing is highly regulated, the rate of harvest does not appear to be sustainable. There are simply too many anglers relative to the number of fish-bearing lakes and streams in Alberta. With the tremendous increase in access throughout the north in recent decades, fish stocks have come under extreme pressure. For example, in Wolfe Lake, 2000 anglers per year caught an average of 0.25 fish per hour in the early 1980s, but by the 1990s 10,000 anglers per year experienced a catch rate of only 0.02 fish per hour (Post et al., 2002). Twenty-one of 27 walleye populations for which data exist have collapsed as a result of overfishing. Pike populations now also show evidence of overexploitation leading to collapse (Post et al., 2002). Finally, arctic grayling and lake sturgeon have each been listed as a species of special concern in Alberta as a result of declining populations and vulnerability to angling pressure and habitat destruction (AEP, 1999).

Forest Industry

At the turn of the 20th century most timber cutting in northern Alberta was for the production of firewood; thus, the overall rate of harvest was negligible. However, incoming settlers created a demand for milled timber, which increased steadily through the early decades of the century. There was also a demand for railway ties created by the rapid expansion of the railway system. The demand for milled timber was met by numerous small mills that were generally located close to their markets. These mills were owned by local families or small businesses and most operated only part-time.

The basic pattern of local mills serving local markets prevailed in northern Alberta throughout the first half of the century. Exports were limited because high rail freight rates effectively made northern lumber uncompetitive in southern markets where cheaper alternative supplies were sufficient to meet existing demand (Wetherell and Kmet, 2000: 347). As a consequence, northern Alberta contributed only a small proportion of provincial lumber output prior to World War II (Wetherell and Kmet, 2000: 346).

The post-war period marked a turning point in the development of the forest industry in Alberta. The War brought the economy out of its prolonged depression and the demand for lumber increased dramatically. By the late 1940s, harvest rates in Alberta were more than three times what they had been during the 1930s (Fig. 2.11). Although most of the expansion occurred in the south, the increased post-war demand, together with decreased transportation costs and increased access, stimulated an expansion of the forest industry in the north as well and initiated

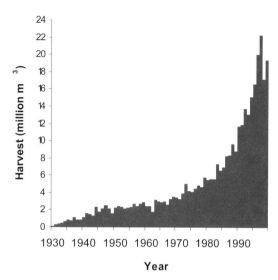

Fig. 2.11. Volume of forest harvested in Alberta, 1930-1999.
Source: Stelfox and Wynes, 1999: 9-17.

a shift towards export markets (Wetherell and Kmet, 2000: 348).

The increased rate of harvest in the post-war period was accompanied by a profound shift in government policy. Prior to this period, regulation of the industry was minimal. Companies generally moved from site to site, selectively removing the largest and most valuable trees. There were no regeneration efforts and no long-term planning for the maintenance of timber flow. This approach seemed acceptable while the overall rate of harvest was low, but as the industry expanded it was felt that a new approach was required that would ensure sustainability of the timber supply. The government also became interested in attracting pulp and paper companies to the province and establishing other large wood processing facilities, such as plywood and chipboard plants (Pratt and Urquhart, 1994: 14). To this

end several important initiatives and changes were implemented:

- the Alberta Forest Service was established (1948), providing the basis for administering and servicing the expanding forestry sector;
- the Green Zone was established (1948), restricting the encroachment of agriculture onto lands best suited for forestry;
- the *Forests Act* was proclaimed (1949) and several new policies were implemented, including area-based agreements, 20-year renewable leases, and sustained-yield management;
- a detailed forest inventory was initiated (1949) to define the available wood supply (a requirement for attracting large forestry projects); and
- a fire suppression system was implemented to protect what was increasingly considered a valuable resource.

The fundamental objective of the new sustained-yield management approach was to ensure a stable flow of timber over a long planning horizon (100 years or more). Simply put, this meant that the rate of harvest in a planning area was not to exceed the rate of forest growth, less losses to natural causes. In order to maximize harvest rates under this regime, forest companies abandoned the practice of selective cutting and began implementing clear-cut harvesting and artificial regeneration (ECA, 1979: 69). In effect, forest stands began to be considered slow-growing crops, amenable to the growth and harvest strategies employed in agricultural settings. Concerns about the habitat needs of wildlife (particularly game species) resulted in the progressive implementation of various restrictions on operating practices;

however, the primacy of timber production remained intact.

The post-war period also marked a transition to greater economies of scale, as efforts were made to increase productivity. Mills and forestry operations became larger and more capital intensive, and increasing use was made of technology and mechanization. As a consequence of these trends, small-scale family-based operations serving local markets were slowly eclipsed by large-scale operations dominated by national or multi-national corporations serving export markets primarily. By the mid-1970s, seven companies processed approximately 80% of the timber cut in Alberta and two-thirds of this output was shipped to the United States (Pratt and Urquhart, 1994: 30).

The next major turning point in the development of Alberta's forest industry came in the late 1980s. A unique alignment of factors during this period resulted in the near-simultaneous development of more than a dozen major wood-processing facilities, including five new pulp mills (Nikiforuk and Struzik, 1989). The bulk of this expansion occurred in northern Alberta where vast tracts of forest were brought into industrial production for the first time (Fig. 2.12). Once the new facilities were fully operational, the rate of harvest in Alberta grew to more than five times what it had been in the 1970s (Fig. 2.11).

A key factor responsible for the forestry developments of the late 1980s was the collapse of oil prices earlier in the decade. This collapse led to government policies that were intended to diversify and stabilize the provincial economy. Forestry, which heretofore had received little attention from the government, was identified as one of the key platforms for diversification. Another important factor in the expansion was that pulping technology had advanced sufficiently by

the 1980s to enable the cost-effective pulping of hardwood species. This was critical because aspen is the most common tree species of northern Alberta. Up to that point aspen had been considered a "weed" species that reduced the desirability of northern forests for large-scale forestry. Finally, after languishing throughout the 1970s, pulp prices rose in the 1980s to the point where the construction of new plants became economically feasible (Pratt and Urquhart, 1994: 51).

The government's plan for expanding the forestry sector in the late 1980s assumed that stable employment and full utilization of the resource (i.e., both hardwoods and softwoods) were paramount. Consequently, a decision was made to focus on large international forestry companies instead of fostering the development of smaller Alberta-based companies (Pratt and Urquhart, 1994: 64). Local companies were not thought to have the capacity, technical knowledge, or capital to operate at the large scale required to make pulp production in northern Alberta viable. In addition, it was felt that large, vertically integrated companies would be better able to weather cyclical downturns in the market. The government also held the assumption that only a short window of opportunity existed before the next downturn in pulp prices would make the construction of new plants uneconomical again (Pratt and Urquhart, 1994: 59).

In order to achieve its expansion objectives within the perceived limited window of opportunity the government dispensed with public hearings, integrated resource planning, and environmental research. Instead, in 1987 it launched a series of closed-door negotiations that resulted in the leasing of timberlands the size of Great Britain, the awarding of $1.2 billion in loan guarantees and debentures, and commitments for

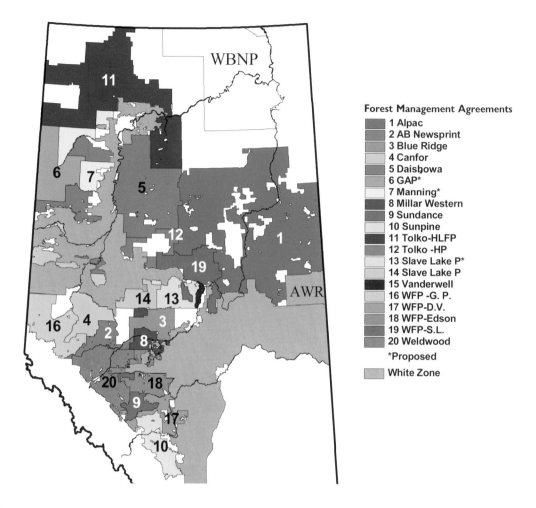

Forest Management Agreements

1 Alpac
2 AB Newsprint
3 Blue Ridge
4 Canfor
5 Daishowa
6 GAP*
7 Manning*
8 Millar Western
9 Sundance
10 Sunpine
11 Tolko-HLFP
12 Tolko -HP
13 Slave Lake P*
14 Slave Lake P
15 Vanderwell
16 WFP -G. P.
17 WFP-D.V.
18 WFP-Edson
19 WFP-S.L.
20 Weldwood
*Proposed
White Zone

Fig. 2.12. Location of Forest Management Agreement areas as of 2000. FMAs 6, 7, and 13 are only in the proposal stage. FMAs 10 and 20 are owned by International Paper Co. FMAs 3, 13 and 14 are owned by West Fraser Forest Products. WFP = Weyerhaeuser Forest Products. AWR = Air Weapons Range. (Map: Forest Watch Alberta)

an additional $170 million in infrastructure development — all in the space of 16 months (Pratt and Urquhart, 1994: 6). The larger projects were eventually subjected to environmental impact assessments; however, this was done in the absence of a cumulative impacts framework. Furthermore, the terms of reference for these assessments were narrowly focussed on the mills, and specifically excluded the impacts of woodland activities (Pratt and Urquhart, 1994: 183).

Despite massive protests and challenges, the initial set of projects proceeded. However, additional planned developments in the 1990s did not, largely due to changing market conditions. The slow-down of the 1990s supports the government's contention that it had to act rapidly in

1987 if the projects were to proceed. The larger issue of whether the rush to develop large pulp and paper mills served the public interest remains to be proven.

Petroleum Industry

The presence of oil in northern Alberta was well known prior to the turn of the 20th century. Bitumen (a semi-solid oil product, like roofing tar) was observed in seeps along the Athabasca River and other locations and was used by natives and explorers to caulk the seams of their birchbark canoes. By the late 1800s the Geological Survey of Canada had already made preliminary explorations in northern Alberta and a few test wells had been drilled (Wetherell and Kmet, 2000: 30). These explorations determined that large deposits of oil sands (a mixture of sand, water, and bitumen) were present, as well as natural gas.

Because conventional oil was not found in the initial surveys, little development of northern petroleum resources was undertaken in the first half of the century. However, the federal and provincial governments did conduct research into commercial applications for bitumen and into the development of efficient methods of processing oil sands (Wetherell and Kmet, 2000: 354). During this period test extraction plants were put into operation near Fort McMurray and some road paving projects were undertaken, but there was no significant commercial production (PCF, 2000: 8-9).

Dramatic changes in the petroleum industry in Alberta occurred after a major oil discovery was made in Leduc in 1947. Other large reservoirs were soon found and these discoveries brought skilled energy industry personnel to Alberta and attracted the attention of international oil companies and investors. An infrastructure of pipelines and refineries was quickly established, and Alberta's oil boom was underway.

Although the initial strikes were made in the south, development of northern petroleum reserves quickly followed. The gas fields in the Peace Country, where access had already been established, were brought into production first. In subsequent decades, petroleum development spread throughout the north, with the exception of the Shield region in the northeast which did not contain petroleum deposits (Fig. 2.13).

The rate of conventional oil and gas development was largely determined by economic factors. When oil and gas prices were high in the 1970s, and again in the 1990s, the rate of drilling increased rapidly (Fig. 2.14). At no time were regulations implemented to limit the pace of petroleum development in order to maintain forest sustainability, even though significant forest impacts had already been identified by the 1970s (ECA, 1979: 27). There was no restriction on the rate of timber cutting for wellsites, seismic exploration, pipelines, or roads, and there was no requirement for forest regeneration (see Chapter 4). Because most petroleum activities resulted in semi-permanent deletions of forest, the cumulative ecological "footprint" of the petroleum industry increased dramatically with each subsequent decade (Figs. 2.7; 2.13-2.16).

The development of the oil sands lagged behind the development of conventional oil and gas reserves, largely because they were more difficult and expensive to recover. The first full-scale commercial operation, the forerunner of today's Suncor Energy Inc., did not begin production until 1967 (PCF, 2000: 10). In 1978, Syncrude began operations, after the federal and provincial governments invested in the project and provided

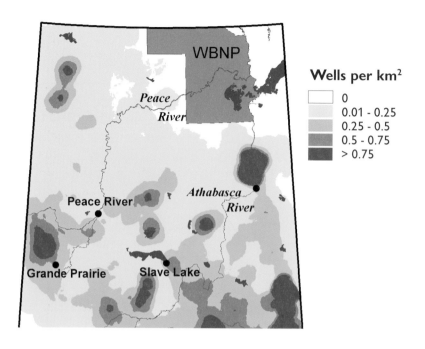

Fig. 2.13. Well density in northern Alberta in 2000. (Map: Forest Watch Alberta)

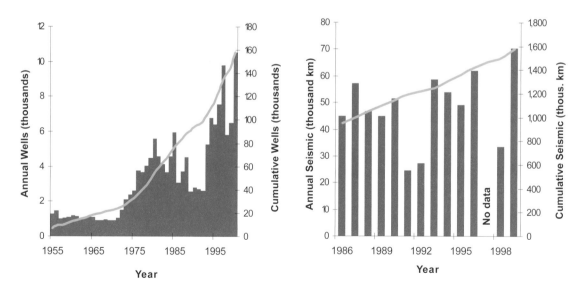

Fig. 2.14. Number of oil and gas wells completed in Alberta, annual (bars) and cumulative (line): 1955-2000. Source: CAPP, 2000.

Fig. 2.15. Length of seismic lines approved in the Green Zone, annual (bars) and cumulative (line): 1986-1999. Source: AEP, 1998b: 79 and ASRD records.

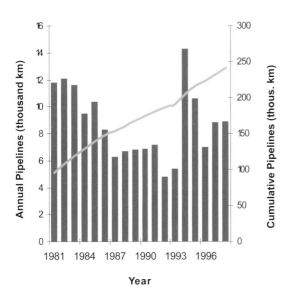

Fig. 2.16. Length of new oil and gas pipelines in Alberta, annual (bars) and cumulative (line): 1981-1998. Source: CAPP, 2000.

assurances about financial terms (PCF, 2000: 10). Both of these operations were essentially mines that extracted oil sands near the surface (Fig. 2.17). Economically-viable techniques for recovering deeply buried oil sands deposits (in-situ bitumen) were subsequently developed, opening a much larger segment of the oil sands deposits to production (Fig. 2.17). Once oil prices recovered in the 1990s, and favourable changes in royalty structure were instituted, development of the oil sands increased dramatically. The total proposed new investment in oil sands projects announced since 1996 now totals over $50 billion (ARD, 2001: 15).

The rapid expansion of the oil sands industry in the late 1990s had many parallels with the expansion of the forest industry in the late 1980s. In the case of the oil sands the government did not offer loan guarantees, but effectively achieved

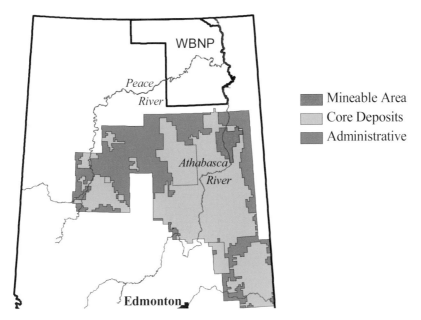

Fig. 2.17. Distribution of oil sands deposits in Alberta, showing total deposits and area amenable to surface mining. Source: AEUB, 2000.

the same result through a reduction of royalty fees (Fig. 2.18). Project approvals were again made in haste, without consideration of the cumulative impacts on the forest. One significant difference from the forestry expansion was that there was relatively little public reaction, perhaps because the individual projects were small relative to the size of the Forest Management Agreements awarded to Alberta-Pacific and Daishowa-Marubeni. The dependence of the province on oil and gas revenues may also have played a role in limiting public reaction.

Other Industries

Other industrial sectors in northern Alberta will not be discussed in detail. Salt mining occurred in the Fort McMurray region early in the century, but is not a significant enterprise at this time. Peat

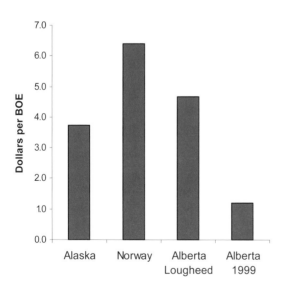

Fig. 2.18. Government oil and gas revenues per barrel of oil equivalent (BOE), in 1996 dollars. Source: MacNab et al., 1999.

harvesting has been expanding, but at present is very limited in extent. There has also been interest in diamond mining in recent years, though no operational mines have been constructed.

Literature Cited

AAFRD (Alberta Agriculture, Food, and Rural Development). 2001. Grazing statistics for public land. (Available at www.agric.gov.ab.ca/index.html)

AEP (Alberta Environmental Protection). 1998a. Northern moose management program progress report. Alberta Environmental Protection, Edmonton, AB. (Available at: www3.gov.ab.ca/srd/fw/hunting/northmoose/98nmoose.html)

AEP (Alberta Environmental Protection). 1998b. The boreal forest natural region of Alberta. Alberta Environmental Protection, Edmonton, AB.

AEP (Alberta Environmental Protection). 1999. The status of Alberta fish. Alberta Environmental Protection, Edmonton, AB. (Available at: www3.gov.ab.ca/srd/fw/fishing/fishstat.html)

AEP (Alberta Environmental Protection). 2000. The general status of Alberta wild species: 2000. Alberta Environmental Protection, Edmonton, AB. (Available at: www3.gov.ab.ca/srd/fw/riskspecies/speciesatrisk/index.html)

AEUB (Alberta Energy and Utilities Board). 2000. Map 90: Designated oil and gas fields, oil sands deposits, main pipelines, refineries, and gas processing plants. Alberta Energy and Utilities Board, Calgary, AB.

AMA (Alberta Municipal Affairs). 2001. 2000 official population list. Alberta Municipal Affairs, Edmonton, AB. (Available at: www3.gov.ab.ca/ma/ms/official_pop_lists.cfm)

ARD (Alberta Resource Development). 2000-2001 annual report. Alberta Resource Development, Edmonton, AB. (Available at: www.energy.gov.ab.ca/com/Room/default.htm)

ASRD (Alberta Sustainable Resource Development). 2001a. Trapping in Alberta. Alberta Sustainable Resource Development, Edmonton, AB. (Available at: www3.gov.ab.ca/srd/fw/trapping/index.html)

ASRD (Alberta Sustainable Resource Development). 2001b. Alberta's furbearers – wolverine. Alberta Sustainable Resource Development, Edmonton, AB. (Available at: www3.gov.ab.ca/srd/fw/trapping/index.html)

ASRD (Alberta Sustainable Resource Development). 2001c. Hunting in Alberta. Alberta Sustainable Resource Development, Edmonton, AB. (Available at: www3.gov.ab.ca/srd/fw/hunting/index.html)

ASRD (Alberta Sustainable Resource Development). 2001d. Fishing in Alberta. Alberta Sustainable Resource Development, Edmonton, AB. (Available at: www3.gov.ab.ca/srd/fw/fishing/index.html)

CAPP (Canadian Association of Petroleum Producers). 2000. Statistical handbook for Canada's upstream petroleum industry. Canadian Association of Petroleum Producers, Calgary, AB.

Carbyn, L. N., S. Oosenbrug, and D. W. Anions. 1993. Wolves, bison, and the dynamics related to the Peace-Athabasca delta in Canada's Wood Buffalo National Park. Canadian Circumpolar Institute, Edmonton, AB.

EC (Environment Canada). 1991. The state of Canada's environment. Environment Canada, Ottawa, ON.

ECA (Environment Council of Alberta). 1979. The environmental effects of forestry operations in Alberta: report and recommendations. Environmental Council of Alberta, Edmonton, AB.

ERCB (Energy Resources Conservation Board). 1992. Report 92-A: Ultimate potential and supply of natural gas in Alberta. Energy Resources Conservation Board, Calgary, AB.

FMHS (Fort McMurray Historical Society). 2001 History of Fort McMurray. Fort McMurray Historical Society. (Available at: www.fortmcmurrayhistory.com/timeline.htm)

Gates, C., T. Chowns, and H. Reynolds. 1992. Wood Buffalo at the crossroads. Pages 139-166 in Foster, J., D. Harrison, and I. MacLaren, editors. Buffalo. University of Alberta Press, Edmonton, AB.

GPCCD (Grande Prairie City Clerk Department). 2001. Population growth. City Clerk Department, Grande Prairie, AB. (Available at: www.city.grande-prairie.ab.ca/pop_grow.htm)

Macnab, B., J. Daniels, and G. Laxer. 1999. Giving away the Alberta advantage: Are Albertans receiving maximum revenues from their oil and gas? Parkland Institute, Edmonton, AB.

McFarlane, B., P. Boxall, and W. Adamowicz. 1998. Big game hunters in Alberta: their activities, values, and preferences in relation to sustainable forest management. Working Paper 1998-4. Sustainable Forest Management Network, Edmonton, AB. (Available at: http://sfm-1.biology.ualberta.ca/english/home/index.htm

Moen, A. 1990. Demystifying forestry law: an Alberta analysis. Environmental Law Centre, Edmonton, AB.

Nikiforuk, A. and E. Struzik. 1989. The great forest sell-off. Report on Business Magazine, 5: 57-67.

PCF (Petroleum Communication Foundation). 2000. Canada's oil sands and heavy oil. Petroleum Communication Foundation, Calgary, AB.

Peterson, S. 1997. Status of the wolverine (Gulo gulo) in Alberta. Alberta Environment, Edmonton, AB. (Available at: www3.gov.ab.ca/srd/fw/status/reports/wolv/index.html)

Post, J. R. and M. Sullivan. 2002. Canada's recreational fisheries: the invisible collapse? Fisheries 27:6-17.

Pratt, L. and I. Urquhart. 1994. The last great forest. NeWest Press, Edmonton, AB.

Revel, R. D., T. D. Dougherty, and D. J. Downing. 1984. forest growth and regeneration along seismic lines. University of Calgary Press, Calgary, AB.

SC (Statistics Canada). 1983. Historical statistics of Canada, 2nd Ed. (Series N38-48). Statistics Canada, Ottawa, ON. (Available at: www.statcan.ca/english/freepub/11-516-XIE/sectiona/toc.htm)

Schneider, R. R. and S. Wasel. 2000. The effect of human settlement on the density of moose in northern Alberta. J. Wildl. Manag. 64:513-520.

Smith, W. and P. Lee. 2000. Canada's forests at a crossroads: an assessment in the year 2000. World Resources Institute, Washington, D.C.

Stelfox, J. B. and B. Wynes. 1999. A physical, biological, and land-use synopsis of the boreal forest's natural regions of northwest Alberta. Daishowa-Marubeni International Ltd., Peace River, AB.

Wetherell, D. and I. Kmet. 2000. Alberta's north: a history, 1890-1950. University of Alberta Press, Edmonton, AB.

Al-Pac

3. The Forestry Sector Today

Overview of the Forest Industry in Alberta

In 1999, the most recent year for which complete data are available, 42,000 ha of forest were harvested in Alberta, producing 19.4 million m³ of timber (CFS, 2001: 29). An additional 7.2 million m³ of fire-killed timber, from the large fires of 1998, was salvage logged in fiscal-year 1999 (ARD, 2000: 52). Even though the volume of timber logged through fire salvage can be large, as in 1999, it is not considered part of the regulated harvest.

Revenue to the Government of Alberta, in the form of timber royalties and fees, was $72.9 million for the fiscal year 2001, offset by government expenditures on forest management and protection (AE, 2001a: 47-48). In 2000, 11,352 people were directly employed in the primary forest sector (logging, lumber mills, pulp and paper, and panelboard) and 11,796 in secondary wood manufacturing (AFPA, 2001). The major export products of the forest industry in Alberta are wood pulp and softwood lumber (Fig. 3.1). The U.S. is the major market for Alberta wood products (Fig. 3.2).

There are three types of timber allocation in Alberta: timber permits, timber quotas, and Forest Management Agreements (FMAs). Timber permits involve relative small volumes intended for smaller operators and community use. Quotas are intended to

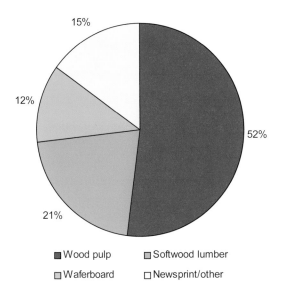

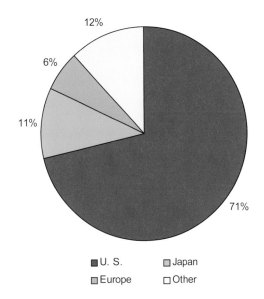

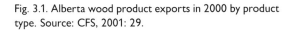

Fig. 3.1. Alberta wood product exports in 2000 by product type. Source: CFS, 2001: 29.

Fig. 3.2. Major export markets for Alberta wood products in 2000. Source: CFS, 2001: 29.

provide small to medium-sized operators with a long-term secure wood supply. As of 1996 there were approximately 50 registered quota holders in Alberta (AEP, 1996: 9). Forest management planning for quota holders is primarily the responsibility of the government. Instead of a fixed land base they are allocated a specific volume of timber.

An FMA is a long-term contractual agreement between the province and a company to establish, grow, and harvest timber on a defined land area (AEP, 1996: 9). As of 2000, 11 companies held one or more FMAs in Alberta and two other FMAs were pending (Fig. 2.12; Table 3.1). FMA holders must develop and follow a management plan that is approved by the government. They are also responsible for their own inventory studies, road development, and forest regeneration.

Provincial Forestry Policy

The Alberta Forest Conservation Strategy

The Alberta Forest Conservation Strategy (AFCS) was developed to fulfill commitments made by the Government of Alberta under the National Forest Strategy. It is the product of over three

Table 3.1. Size of FMAs of the 5 largest companies in Alberta in 2000. Source: Forest Watch Alberta.

Company	Size of FMA (km²)
Alpac	58,000
Tolko[1]	39,400
Weyerhaeuser[1]	29,648
Daishowa-Marubeni	29,000
International Paper[1]	16,949

[1]Multiple FMAs

years of work by an 11-member multi-stake-holder steering committee, a stakeholder advisory group (representing over 60 stakeholder groups), urban and rural working groups, and strategic issues working groups. In total, over 800 Albertans participated in the development of the *Strategy*. Given this broad representation and concerted effort, the AFCS is the best available guide to the vision and goals held by Albertans regarding public forests.

A fundamental principle of the AFCS is that forest ecosystem health must be maintained if we are to continue to receive benefits from the forest in the future (AFCSSC, 1997, p. 4):

The forests of Alberta will be appreciated as ecosystems and our activities managed in ways that conserve ecological integrity, biological diversity, long-term forest productivity and the forest landbase.

To maintain ecosystem health the AFCS recommends *"that the Government of Alberta and forest land users adopt and implement ecosystem-based forest management as quickly as practicable."* (AFCSSC, 1997, p. 11). The key elements of ecological forest management (EFM) include harvesting that emulates natural disturbances (the natural disturbance model), adaptive management (changing management plans in response to feedback from the system), protected area benchmarks (for monitoring and risk management), public involvement in decision-making, and application of the precautionary principle (erring on the side of caution when the consequences of actions are uncertain). A large body of scientific literature is now available regarding EFM (reviewed in Chapters 6 and 7).

Current Government Policy

The *Forests Act* provides the legal framework for the management of forests in Alberta (GOA, 1999). It defines the basic rules governing forest tenure and provides the Minister and Cabinet with the power to set policies and regulations governing logging methods, wood utilization standards, and broader issues concerning use of forest land (Moen, 1990, p. 8). The *Act* itself provides minimal guidance as to how the forests should be managed, except that the harvesting of timber should be designed to provide a perpetual sustained yield (GOA, 1999, sec. 16(1)).

Given the limited scope of the *Forests Act*, governance of forest management in Alberta is primarily conducted through policy directives, not law. Consequently, major management decisions are not subject to legislative debate, nor can the government be held legally accountable for its management of the forest.

An overview of current provincial forestry policy is found in *The Alberta Forest Legacy* (AEP, 1998a), produced in response to the AFCS. The *Alberta Forest Legacy* accepts the vision, goals, and principles of the AFCS (AEP, 1998a, p. 7); however, it provides little direction for actual implementation and is largely devoid of explicit commitments or measurable objectives. Five years after the completion of the AFCS, a plan for implementation is still lacking.

The shift in forestry policy embodied in the *Alberta Forest Legacy* has not yet resulted in substantive change at the operational level. The existing rules and regulations are still fundamentally based on the concept of sustained-yield management. What sustained-yield management means in practical terms is that the annual rate of cut cannot exceed the annual rate of tree growth, less losses due to natural causes (AEP, 1996, p. 4). The concept was developed at a time when forests were valued primarily for their timber; therefore, there are no explicit requirements to maintain ecosystem integrity or to conserve biodiversity. The objective is to sustain the flow of timber, not the forest itself.

Quota holders and FMA holders typically operate within the same forests (utilizing different tree species), but different systems of management apply to each. In the case of quota holders, harvest planning and operating practices are directed by the *Alberta Timber Harvest Planning and Operating Ground Rules* (AEP, 1994). For FMA holders, basic requirements are defined in the individual FMA contracts. Each FMA holder must also develop a detailed forest management plan that is approved by the government (see below). An additional complication of the existing system is that all commercial forest stands are permanently designated as either coniferous or deciduous, and different rules regarding allocation and management apply to each.

In summary, although the provincial government has accepted the goals and principles of the AFCS, it has taken no substantive action with respect to implementation. Instead, there is every indication that the government remains fundamentally committed to policies set in the late 1980s of full utilization of the forest and maximization of economic returns. For example:

1. Government business plans continue to include targets such as "*Sustain growth opportunities in the forest sector through maximization of the wood fibre opportunity*" and "*Increase the timber cut and reduce the gap between the harvest and the Annual Allowable Cut (AAC) cap.*" (ARD, 2001: 43).

2. The Annual Allowable Cut and new forest allocations continue to be based on sustained-yield management, progressively removing what little flexibility remains in the system.

3. The regulation of harvest practices continues to be based on sustained-yield management, lagging substantially behind the changes being proposed by many FMA holders in the province (see below). Moreover, the efforts of progressive FMA holders to implement new management techniques are hampered by the outdated government regulations, that include requirements for total utilization.

4. As part of proposed revisions to the provincial operating ground rules the government is considering to allow harvesting within riparian areas (AE, 2001b). These areas are currently classified as environmentally sensitive and harvesting is not permitted.

5. Government permits for the application of herbicides have risen from almost none in 1994 to over 30,000 ha in 1999 (Fig. 3.3). This reflects a general trend to intensive forest management, in place of progress towards EFM.

Another likely reason for the government's lack of action is that earlier policies have left little flexibility in the system for change. Virtually all of the coniferous land base and most of the deciduous land base have been allocated on the basis of the old system of sustained-yield management (Fig. 3.4). The overall rate of harvest is nearing full utilization on this basis (Fig. 3.5). Consequently, a reduction in cut levels, as required to implement certain features of EFM (such as maintaining older age classes of forest or retain-

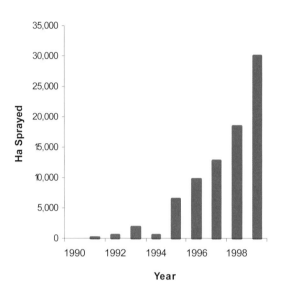

Fig. 3.3. Amount of forest in Alberta sprayed with herbicides, 1990-1999. Source: CFS, 2002: Table 9.2.

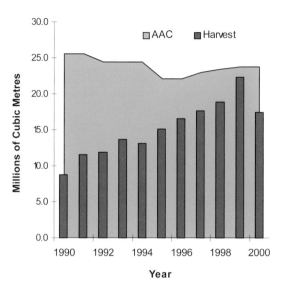

Fig. 3.5. Annual allowable cut (AAC) and actual harvest levels in Alberta from 1991 to 2000. 1999 value includes fire salvage, 2000 value does not. Source: ARD, 2000: 52.

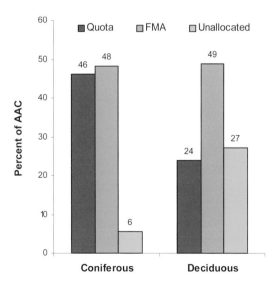

Fig. 3.4. Allocation of the annual allowable cut (AAC) in Alberta, under sustained-yield management, as of 1995. Source: AEP, 1996:16.

ing live trees on harvest blocks), would be resisted by many existing forestry companies on the basis of existing rights. Simulation studies by Cumming and Armstrong (1999) have demonstrated that timber supplies to existing companies could likely be maintained by eliminating inefficiencies associated with the current system of overlapping tenures and dual land bases. However, this would entail a major overhaul of the tenure system — an undertaking that may be giving the government cause to hesitate.

Harvest Planning and Practices

Overview

The information provided in this section was primarily derived from a survey of FMA holders conducted by Forest Watch Alberta in the fall of

2000 (FWA, 2001). The survey was based on information contained in the most recent detailed forest management plans submitted by FMA holders to the government. These plans provide only an approximation of actual practices because (1) plans and projections provided by the companies are often overly optimistic relative to what is actually implemented on the ground, and (2) some companies are in the process of updating their plans. Although the government monitors compliance with certain regulations (e.g., cutblock size), a complete audit of a company's performance relative to its management plan is not required.

The management plans vary tremendously in terms of format and content. Although the *Interim Forest Management Planning Manual* (AEP, 1998b) was developed to help guide and standardize the development of management plans, it does not appear to have had any appreciable impact on the plans that have been developed since its release.

In the Forest Watch Alberta survey it was apparent that the language of EFM is becoming widely adopted by forestry companies across the province (Table 3.2). However, only Alpac and Daishowa-Marubeni have management plans that are actually based on EFM principles, as described in the AFCS and scientific literature (albeit, with various shortcomings). Not coincidentally, Alpac and Daishowa are both deciduous operators working on a virgin land base that provides them with the flexibility required to implement EFM. Weyerhaeuser has also embraced EFM, but its transition from sustained-yield management is less advanced. Canfor, Millar Western, and Weldwood, are in transition from sustained-yield management to alternative systems of their own design. These three companies

plan to implement some of the elements of EFM, but there remains a strong emphasis on the use of indicator species and habitat modelling to achieve locally defined forest management objectives (contrary to the spirit and intent of the AFCS). Sundance and Sunpine also appear to be in transition to EFM; however, their plans are grossly deficient with respect to ecological targets and implementation strategies. Alberta Newsprint, Tolko, and West Fraser continue to pursue sustained-yield management and declined to provide any details regarding their future plans when surveyed.

Quota holders continue to be managed by the Department of Resource Development on the basis of sustained-yield management, using the *Alberta Timber Harvest Planning and Operating Ground Rules* (AEP, 1994). The *Ground Rules* were developed in 1994 and contain no mention of EFM, nor do they incorporate any form of long-term landscape-level planning. Because quota holders account for almost half of the coniferous harvest, and a third of the deciduous harvest (Fig. 3.4), and because two of the largest FMA holders remain committed to sustained-yield (Tolko and West Fraser), the majority of the timber in Alberta continues to be harvested under sustained-yield management. The government is currently in the process of updating the *Ground Rules*, but it has set an extended six-year timeline for doing so (AEP, 2000). It is unclear to what extent EFM principles will be incorporated in the new *Ground Rules*.

Alpac, Daishowa, and Weyerhaeuser appear to understand EFM well, and their management objectives are reasonably comprehensive. However, the implementation strategies proposed by these companies are incompletely developed and there is considerable doubt as to whether their stated objectives can be achieved. In particular, traditional harvest models (Woodstock and Stanley) continue to be used to select and schedule forest stands for harvest, even though these models cannot incorporate ecological outcomes or the potential impacts of wildfire (Baskent, 1999).

In place of active ecosystem-based planning, these companies hope to achieve ecological objectives primarily through ad hoc measures. These measures are likely to succeed in adding variability into the system, but will fall significantly short of emulating the distributions and patterns that are actually produced by natural disturbances. For example, even without explicit planning, some old-growth will be retained on the landscape due to inoperable sites, isolated stands, and riparian buffers. However, the amount of old-growth, its distribution on the landscape, and the size of patches, will not be the same under this "default" approach as the patterns produced by natural disturbances (Ohman and Eriksson, 1998). The plans of these companies represent an important step in the right direction, but are still a long way from true EFM (see Chapters 6 and 7).

Stand-level Practices

Conventional harvesting is based on a two-pass clearcut system in which half of the merchantable timber in an operating area is removed in an initial cut, and the remaining timber is removed after the initial cutblocks have regenerated to a prescribed standard (AEP, 1994: sec 2.2). Under the traditional system cutblocks are generally square and of fixed size, leading to a "checkerboard" pattern (Fig 3.6).

Most FMA holders have now adopted the objective of maintaining natural patterns in stand shape and size, in place of the "checkerboard"

harvest, on the basis of EFM principles. Companies generally plan to achieve this objective through whole-stand harvesting (though cutting is still generally done in two passes, because of provincial regulations). This approach will introduce much-needed variability into the system, but additional effort will be required to overcome constraints on the minimum and maximum size of cutblocks so that the natural distribution of stand sizes can be fully achieved. Additional effort will also be required to counteract the impact of linear disturbances, such as seismic lines and roads, which reduce the average size of stands through fragmentation.

Another feature of conventional clearcut harvesting is that the cutblock is largely devoid of residual structure after the completion of cutting. In order to maintain structure within stands, as

Fig. 3.6. Traditional "checkerboard" harvest pattern (Twp 34, Rge 7, W5th; dimension of photo = 2.8 x 2.8 km; taken in 1992). (Photo: Air Photo Services, Alberta Sustainable Resource Development)

Table 3.2. General management approach of FMA holders in Alberta. Source: Extracted from Detailed Forest Management Plans and other company documents.

Company	General approach to forest management
Alberta-Pacific Forest Industries (Alpac)	The objective of forest **ecosystem management** is to reduce the risk to the forest ecosystem by developing strategies that will maintain biodiversity. Harvesting, following an ecosystem management approach, should approximate the historical structure and pattern of vegetation at the regional, landscape and stand levels. The goal is to approximate fire effects as closely as possible within the bounds of economic, social, cultural and ecological influences. Using this approach there is no need for species specific wildlife management strategies except where species might be considered at risk (i.e., woodland caribou) or to accommodate overriding social demands.
Alberta Newsprint Company (ANC)	This FMA area is being managed with great care to supply a renewable, **sustained yield** of wood fibre in perpetuity. ANC is committed to the use of sound, progressive forest management strategies to ensure our long term wood supply and the health of the lands in our care.
Canadian Forest Products (Canfor)	Canfor will use forest **ecosystem management** that encompasses entire forest landscapes and that forecasts the future condition of forests for 100 years or more. The use of a forest ecosystem model allows correctly formulated anthropogenic disturbances to replace natural disturbance processes. Seven species of special management concern were selected for **HSI modeling** or habitat constraint modeling. These seven species were selected because they represent a broad and variable range of habitat characteristics. Thus, if the habitat is maintained and available for these species, it is assumed that the FMA will contain a wide range of habitat conditions suitable for all other species in the planning area.
Daishowa-Marubeni International (DMI)	This approach was derived from the **ecological management** approach developed in the *Alberta Forest Conservation Strategy*. The ecological management approach is to design human disturbances (like harvesting) in a way that they can replicate some of the effects of natural disturbances, and to place them on the landscape in a way that they can contribute towards the production of a desired future forest state. The approach assumes that the future forest, if it is similar in structure and function to the historical natural forest, should support a similar range of biological life. No specific objectives are set for individual habitat types or individual species; rather, the approach minimizes the risk of loss of habitats or species in the absence of sufficient knowledge to manage for them.
International Paper - Sunpine	Conduct forestry practices which maintain a **sustained yield** of timber from the productive forest land while adhering to the principles of **ecological forest management**. Focus on maintaining diversity at both the landscape and stand levels and approximating natural processes. In general, the intent will be to approximate the natural distribution of stand ages, size and structure.
International Paper - Weldwood	Commitment to practice sustainable forest management as defined by the Canadian Council of Forest Ministers (1992). **Habitat supply modeling** used to ensure that no habitat supply bottlenecks occur at the FMA scale for any of the modeled species. 30 species selected to represent each of 16 terrestrial associations.

Table 3.2 (Continued)

Company	General approach to forest management
Weldwood (cont.)	Harvesting within the limits of regeneration and natural growth in a manner that preserves the diversity of complex and interlinked ecosystems.
Millar Western	The preferred strategy represents the most feasible approach to meet the forest-level goals and objectives derived from a public involvement process. **Biodiversity indicator forecasts** for each strategy will be analyzed, compared and eval-uated, leading to reformulation and retesting of management strategies. This process continues until an acceptable management strategy is achieved. Since MWI is facing a shortage of fibre for its mills, an **enhanced silviculture strategy** has been developed to increase (almost double) the annual allowable cut from the landbase.
Sundance	The timber supply analysis procedure for the Sundance FMA was designed to meet the wood supply needs of the company while meeting or exceeding current provincial management standards. Agreement to establish, grow, harvest, and remove timber on a **sustainable basis**. The future forest will resemble the existing forest in terms of species composition as closely as possible given the need for access and resource extraction. Effects of fire will be partially emulated.
Tolko - High Prairie - High Level	Tolko is committed to evolving towards sustainable forest management from the current principle of **sustained yield management** with multiple objectives. Over-all, Tolko's corporate goals are consistent with the objectives of the *Alberta Forest Legacy* and include: sustainable forest management and the consideration of a broad range of forest values in the development of effective forest mgmt. strategies.
West Fraser - Blue Ridge Lumber	Blue Ridge Lumber will be moving from a **sustained yield** to an ecologically based approach of sustainable forest management. Harvesting the older, high-risk timber is a high priority and is required to maintain a healthy forest.
West Fraser - Slave Lake Pulp	Achieve and maintain a perpetual, **sustained yield** of timber while not diminishing the productivity of the forest land. Slave Lake Pulp believes that management of the timber resources within the FMA needs to take place in a manner that recognizes and protects biodiversity within an objective range of natural variability. Strategies will be developed during the term of this plan to provide for forest sustainability through management of vegetation associations. Place priority on planning and conducting harvest operations on sites containing stands of overmature, decadent timber.
Weyerhaeuser Forest Products (WFP): - Drayton Valley - Edson - Grande Prairie - Slave Lake	Weyerhaeuser Canada is committed to the conservation of biological diversity and the long-term sustainability of managed forest ecosystems. The long-term sustainability of forest ecosystems and the ecological requirements of most species can be achieved by mimicking the natural process of disturbance and succession that are characteristic of a site or region. In **ecologically-based forest management**, planning for future forest landscapes means maintaining a range of age structures, seral stages, and abundance of forest cover types that are characteristic of each Subregion.

prescribed by EFM, most companies now plan to retain snags and downed logs on harvest sites. Some companies are also distributing logging debris on the harvest site; however, the burning of debris is still common. The retention of live clumps of trees after harvest has received the least attention, presumably because there is a direct impact on harvest volume. Daishowa's technical committee determined that 15% of merchantable timber should be retained on harvest blocks to achieve ecological objectives at the stand level, and this value was subsequently set as the company's target (DMI, 1999). But 15% retained structure is substantially less than what typically remains after a fire; therefore, it remains to be determined whether this target will in fact be sufficient. The management plans of most other FMA holders have no target at all for live-tree retention, and of the few that do, targets are between 1-5%.

In Alberta all merchantable stands are designated as either coniferous or deciduous based on the volume of conifer at the time of initial inventory, and managed separately, generally by different operators (Cumming and Armstrong, 1999). Regeneration efforts are, by regulation, intended to produce relatively pure stands of either deciduous or coniferous trees, depending on the initial land base designation. Most coniferous sites continue to be regenerated using monoculture plantation techniques, including invasive site preparation, planting of genetically selected seedlings, and mechanical or chemical control of competing vegetation (Fig. 3.3). The regeneration of most deciduous sites is accomplished through natural regeneration.

There are two major problems with the current system of regeneration. First, the intensive techniques used on coniferous sites (Fig. 3.7) cause significant disruption of the soil and of

natural forest processes (Easton and Martin, 1998; Stelfox et al., 2000). This represents a significant risk to the maintenance of forest integrity. Second, the focus on producing pure deciduous and coniferous stands implies the liquidation of the mixedwood stand type. Mixedwood stands are structurally complex and play a critical role in supporting the biodiversity of Alberta's boreal forest (Stelfox, 1995: *viii*).

A working group was recently established in Alberta for the purpose of developing and refining so-called "mixedwood management" techniques. Under mixedwood management, deciduous and coniferous trees regenerate together on the same site, with minimal intervention (see Chapter 6). Several issues pertaining to government regeneration standards, the dual land base system, and integration between FMA holders and quota holders must first be resolved before mixedwood management can be implemented on a wide scale.

Fig. 3.7. Mound scarifier, used in preparing ground prior to planting conifers. (Photo: D. Mussell)

Because they are outdated, the provincial *Ground Rules* do not incorporate mixedwood management or any of the other practices related to EFM. In the *Ground Rules*, the regulations pertaining to forest protection are focussed on watershed protection (via buffer strip prescriptions), mitigation of the impacts of road construction, and the maintenance of habitat for game species.

Landscape-level Planning

Under the conventional sustained-yield harvest system, the rate of harvest and the selection of stands is based on the objective of sustaining an even flow of timber over a long planning horizon. There are no additional landscape-level objectives.

One of the key attributes to be maintained at the landscape level under EFM is the natural age structure of the forest (Bergeron et al., 1999). Of greatest concern is the proportion of old-growth, as old-growth stands have the highest levels of species diversity but are destined for liquidation under sustained-yield management (Stelfox, 1995: *vi*; Burton et al., 1999). The two most progressive deciduous operators, Alpac and Daishowa, have deciduous old-growth targets of only 8%, which is substantially less than the current proportion of old-growth on the landscape (see Chapter 8). The average old-growth targets of Weyerhaeuser are even lower, and most of the remaining companies have not defined any targets for merchantable old-growth. The provincial *Ground Rules* specify that 10% of all management units must be retained in mature or overmature forest; however, this may be achieved using "*unmerchantable stands, watercourse protection buffers, and other areas not scheduled for harvest*" (AEP, 1994: sec. 4.3.2).

Another core element of EFM at the landscape level is the maintenance of natural patterns in the spatial distribution of forest stands (Baskent, 1999). Although FMA holders implementing EFM all include this as an objective, implementation is again limited to passive measures such as whole-stand harvesting. This is not the same as the natural disturbance model, which involves developing a detailed description of the natural patterns and then actively selecting harvest blocks to achieve targets based on these patterns in perpetuity. The spatial distribution of old-growth patches, especially the larger ones, is at significant risk of being altered without such active management (Ohman and Eriksson, 1998). As expected, most companies without a strong commitment to EFM have no targets for landscape patterns. The provincial operating ground rules are likewise mute on this issue.

The final element of EFM at the landscape level is the maintenance of stand types. Those companies implementing EFM include the maintenance of natural proportions of stand types as an objective. However, realization of this objective requires the successful implementation of mixedwood management. Companies that are not committed to EFM do not include targets for maintaining natural proportions of stand types.

Other Issues

A serious deficiency common to the management plans of all FMA holders is that they fail to account for changes to the forest beyond those resulting from harvesting operations. For example, given current rates of burning it is certain that large fires will sporadically occur in each of the FMAs over the typical 200-year planning horizon. However, there is no mention in any of the plans of how ecological attributes of the forest will be maintained under the combined impact of forest harvesting and wildfire. Similarly, the ecological impact of oil and gas exploration and extraction is ignored in all of the management plans, even though the oil and gas industry annually disturbs almost the same area of forest as the forest industry (see Chapter 4). Most oil and gas industry disturbance arises from seismic exploration and road development and has the effect of (1) increasing the proportion of young forest (by removing mature trees), (2) reducing the average patch size (through fragmentation), and (3) increasing human access to the forest. Unless FMA holders account for these impacts, the implementation of EFM cannot succeed. Indeed, success in achieving ecological objectives will likely be possible only if the oil and gas industry also adopts EFM (involving changes in practices) and enters into integrated planning with FMA holders.

Under the current management system, every merchantable forest stand in Alberta that is part of the allocated land base (i.e., virtually all of the Green Zone), will eventually have a road constructed to it (Fig. 3.8). Indeed, expenditures on road development have been growing rapidly in recent years (Fig. 3.9). These roads result in the loss and fragmentation of habitat, changes in animal movement patterns, soil erosion, disruption of water and fish movements, and increased access by humans (resulting in increased hunting and poaching) (Trombulak and Frissell, 2000). Many FMA holders plan to decommission local haul roads leading to individual stands once harvesting is complete; however, once roads are constructed it is very difficult to prevent all-terrain vehicles and snowmobiles from accessing an area. Furthermore, it is only the short in-block roads

Fig. 3.8. Logging access road under construction. (Photo: Canadian Parks and Wilderness Society - Edmonton)

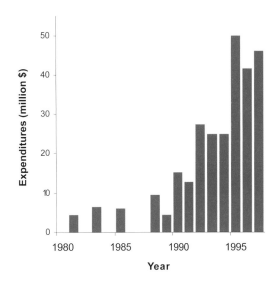

Fig. 3.9. Expenditures on forest access development by the forestry sector in Alberta, 1980-1997. Source: CFS, 2002: Table 7.2.

that are being decommissioned. The main arterial road network that is being constructed to provide access throughout Alberta's forests is intended to be permanent. There is no mention in any of the management plans of alternatives to such a permanent dispersed road network.

Most FMA holders that harvest coniferous trees intend to implement at least some elements of intensive forest management (also known as enhanced forest management) on their FMAs. Intensive forest management involves the application of techniques to increase the growth rate of forest stands (AEP, 1997: 1), at the cost of disrupting natural processes (Easton and Martin, 1998). The growing trend toward intensive management is not being offset by increases in protected areas or the advancement of EFM, and hence is a serious cause for concern.

Public Involvement

In addition to changes in operating practices, the AFCS calls for changes in the way that decisions are made about the use of our forests. Specifically, the AFCS recommends that, "*meaningful public involvement must be an integral component of all major decisions*" (AFCSSC, 1997: 24).

Five years after the release of the AFCS, there is no evidence of substantive change in the way major timber allocations and policy decisions are made. A case in point is the proposed Grande Alberta Paper FMA in northwestern Alberta. The proposed FMA overlaps the last opportunity for the establishment of a large protected area in the northern Foothills Natural Region, of which less than 2% is currently protected. Despite this land use conflict, and several other concerns involving the public interest (Walsh, 2000), negotiations have all been conducted privately between the government and the industrial proponent. Not only has the public been excluded from involvement, but information regarding the negotiations can be obtained only through challenge under the Freedom of Information process (M. Wenig, pers. comm.).

In recent planning processes that have involved substantial public consultation the government has established a record of disregarding the public will. The Special Places 2000 process and the AFCS itself are prime examples of this. As a consequence, instead of progress towards "meaningful public involvement", the situation in Alberta is one of growing polarization between groups representing public forest interests and the government.

FMA holders are required to incorporate public involvement into their development of management plans. Typically, this is accomplished through the input from permanent public advisory committees that are organized and supported by the FMA holders. In practice, the success of public advisory committees in ensuring that the goals and principles of the AFCS are incorporated into management plans is limited by several factors. First, most advisory committees are dominated by forest "user" groups and local economic interests, and there is little or no representation of interests pertaining to the conservation of biodiversity. Second, forest management has become very complex, involving much technical detail. Public advisory groups generally do not have the technical capacity necessary to independently analyze, critique, and offer alternatives to proposals made by the FMA holder. This problem is exacerbated by the fact that advisory committees rely on the FMA holder as their primary source of information. Finally, the scope of advisory committee discussions is constrained by limits imposed by the FMA holder and existing forestry policy. For example, it is assumed that existing mills are to be used at full capacity. Advisory committees are expected to work within this constraint, even though under EFM it is the forest's capacity to supply timber that is supposed to define harvest rates, not the requirements of existing mills.

Another issue related to public involvement in decision-making is access to information. The AFCS recommends that "*all of the information used in planning and decision-making processes should be available to those who wish to be involved*" (AFCSSC, 1997: 23). In reality, Alberta remains a difficult jurisdiction in which to obtain information on forestry. Gaining access to forest management plans is generally problematic, even though the Internet provides an obvious mechanism for facilitating access. Forest inventory data, now that it is being collected by the FMA holders instead of the government, is considered proprietary information and, therefore, not publicly available. Finally, in contrast to many other jurisdictions (especially in the U.S.) basic digital maps compiled by the government using tax dollars (such as the boundaries of FMAs) are not provided to the public as a free service.

Literature Cited

AE (**Alberta Environment**). 2001a. Annual report 2000/2001. Alberta Environment, Edmonton, AB. (Available at: www.gov.ab.ca/env/dept/).

AE (**Alberta Environment**). 2001b. Riparian management models. Supplement #4 in: Draft guidelines to Alberta ground rules renewal. Alberta Environment, Edmonton, AB.

AEP (**Alberta Environmental Protection**). 1994. Alberta timber harvest planning and ground rules. Alberta Environmental Protection, Edmonton, AB. (Available at: www.gov.ab.ca/env/forests.html)

AEP (**Alberta Environmental Protection**). 1996. The status of Alberta's timber supply. Alberta Environmental Protection, Edmonton, AB. (Available at: www.gov.ab.ca/env/forests.html)

AEP (**Alberta Environmental Protection**). 1997. Policy requirements for implementation: report of the Enhanced Forest Management Task Force. Alberta Environmental Protection, Edmonton, AB.

AEP (**Alberta Environmental Protection**). 1998a. The Alberta forest legacy. Alberta Environmental Protection, Edmonton, AB. (Available at: www.gov.ab.ca/env/forests.html).

AEP (**Alberta Environmental Protection**). 1998b. Interim forest management planning manual - guidelines to plan development (ver. 4.1). Alberta Environmental Protection, Edmonton, AB. (Available at: www.gov.ab.ca/env/forests.html).

AEP (**Alberta Environmental Protection**). 2000. A strategy for ground rules renewal. Alberta Environmental Protection, Edmonton, AB. (Available at: www3.gov.ab.ca/srd/forests/).

AFCSSC (**Alberta Forest Conservation Strategy Steering Committee**). 1997. Alberta forest conservation strategy. Alberta Environmental Protection, Edmonton, AB. (Available at: www.borealcentre.ca/reports/reports.html).

AFPA (**Alberta Forest Products Association**). 2001. Alberta forest products industries: overview of economic impact. Alberta Forest Products Association, Edmonton, AB.

ARD (**Alberta Resource Development**). 2000. Annual report 1999/2000. Alberta Resource Development, Edmonton, AB. (Available at: www3.gov.ab.ca/srd/forests)

ARD (**Alberta Resource Development**). 2001. Annual report 2000/2001. Alberta Resource Development, Edmonton, AB. (Available at: www3.gov.ab.ca/srd/forests)

Baskent, E. 1999. Controlling spatial structure of forested landscapes: a case study towards landscape management. Land. Ecol. 14:83-97.

Bergeron, Y., B. Harvey, A. Leduc, and S. Gauthier. 1999. Forest management guidelines based on natural disturbance dynamics: stand and forest-level considerations. For. Chron. 75:49-54.

Burton, P., D. Kneeshaw, and D. Coates. 1999. Managing forest harvesting to maintain old growth in boreal and sub-boreal forests. For. Chron. 75:623-631.

CFS (**Canadian Forest Service**). 2001. The state of Canada's forests: 2000/2001. Canadian Forest Service, Ottawa, ON. (Available at: http://nrcan.gc.ca/cfs/proj/ppiab/sof/common/latest.shtml).

Alternative Futures

CFS (**Canadian Forest Service**). 2002. National forestry database, on-line, Canadian Forestry Service, Ottawa, ON. (Available at: http://nfdp.ccfm.org/framesinv_e.htm)

Cumming, S. and G. Armstrong. 1999. Divided land bases and overlapping tenures in Alberta's boreal forests: a simulation study of policy alternatives. Working Paper 1999-3, Sustainable Forest Management Network, Edmonton, AB. (Available at: http://sfm-1. biology.ualberta.ca/english/home/index.htm).

DMI (Daishowa-Marubeni International) 1999. Detailed forest management plan: 1999-2009. Daishowa-Marubeni International, Peace River, AB.

Easton, W. E. and K. Martin. 1998. The effect of vegetation management on breeding bird communities in British Columbia. Ecol. Appl. 8:1092-1103.

FWA (Forest Watch Alberta). 2001. Planning and practices survey of Forest Management Agreement holders in Alberta. Forest Watch Alberta, Edmonton, AB. (Available at: www.forestwatchalberta.ca)

GOA (Government of Alberta). 1999. The forests act. Queen's Printer for Alberta, Edmonton, AB. (Available at: www.gov.ab.ca/qp/).

Moen, A. 1990. Demystifying forestry law: an Alberta analysis. Environmental Law Centre, Edmonton, AB.

Ohman, K. and L. Eriksson. 1998. The core area concept in forming contiguous areas for long-term forest planning. Can. J. For. Res. 28:1032-1039.

Stelfox, J. B. 1995. Relationships between stand age, stand structure, and biodiversity in aspen mixedwood forests in Alberta. Alberta Environmental Centre, Vegreville, AB. (Available at: www.borealcentre.ca/reports/reports.html).

Stelfox, J. G., J. B. Stelfox, W. Bessie, and C. Clark. 2000. Long-term (1956-1996) effects of clearcut logging and scarification on forest structure and biota in spruce, mixedwood, and pine communities of west-central Alberta. (Available at: www.borealcentre.ca/reports/reports.html)

Trombulak, S. and C. Frissell. 2000. Review of ecological effects of roads on terrestrial and aquatic communities. Cons. Biol. 14:18-30.

Walsh, H. 2000. Alberta's Chinchaga wilderness. Albertans for a Wild Chinchaga, Fairview, AB. (Available at: www.telusplanet.net/public/bwalsh/)

4. The Petroleum Sector Today

Overview of the Petroleum Industry in Alberta

In 2000, Alberta's oil and gas infrastructure consisted of 103,806 operating wells, 293,799 km of pipelines, and 684 gas plants (ARD, 2001: 33). Alberta also has a large petrochemical industry that upgrades raw petroleum resources into ethylene, methanol, ammonia, and other derivative products. In 2000, Alberta produced 55% of Canada's conventional oil, 83% of natural gas, and 100% of bitumen and synthetic crude oil (ARD, 2001: 14).

In 2000, Alberta exported more than $35 billion of oil, gas, and petroleum byproducts, representing 62% of all provincial exports (ARD, 2001: 14). Disposition of Alberta's oil production in 1999 was 58% to the United States, 14% to the rest of Canada, and 27% for use within Alberta (ARD, 2000: 2). Disposition of Alberta's natural gas in 1999 was 47% to the United States, 31% to the rest of Canada, and 22% within Alberta (ARD, 2000: 3).

There are approximately 950 active oil and gas companies in Alberta (ARD, 2001: 33). Although large integrated companies and senior producers account for only about 5% of the companies (NRC, 1995), they produce the majority of the oil and gas in the province (Fig. 4.1; Table 4.1). Consequently, they are responsible for the majority

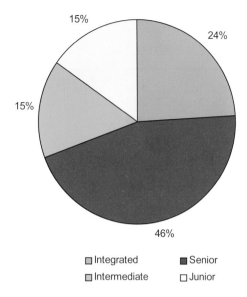

Fig. 4.1. Oil and gas production in Canada in 1994 by company category. Junior < 0.5; Intermediate = 0.5-1.5; Senior > 1.5 mm3/year. Source: NRC, 1995.

Table 4.1. Ranking of the 11 largest petroleum companies operating in western Canada, by proved oil and gas reserves in 2000[1].

Company	BOE[2](millions)
Imperial	1,919
ExxonMobil	1,916
Can. Nat. Res.	1,035
PanCanadian	1,017
Shell	817
Husky Energy	799
Petro Canada	763
Gulf	753
Talisman	612
Alberta Energy	596
Suncor	585

[1]Data from company annual reports (Canadian operations). International and off-shore reserves were excluded (except ExxonMobil).

[2]BOE = Barrel of oil equivalent.

of the environmental impacts associated with oil and gas activities. However, the impacts of junior producers may be disproportionately high relative to their production rates. This is because junior companies lack the resources of larger companies for implementing the highest standard of environmental practices and they are less exposed to public and regulatory scrutiny (Marr-Laing and Severson-Baker, 1999).

Industry expenditures are fairly evenly divided between exploration, development, extraction operations, and royalties (Fig. 4.2). In 1999, capital expenditures by the energy industry were almost $11 billion, representing over 30% of total capital investment in the province (ARD, 2000: 5; PCF, 2000). Approximately 70,000 people are directly employed in Alberta's upstream petroleum industry (SC, 2002).

In the fiscal year 2000/2001, provincial revenues from oil and gas royalties, tenure sales, and fees totalled an unprecedented $10.7 billion, representing 50.5% of total provincial revenues (ARD, 2001: 74) (Fig. 4.3). In the three previous years the petroleum sector contributed an average of 25.3% of provincial revenues (PCF, 2000).

Tenure System

Petroleum deposits are found throughout Alberta except in the Shield Region in the northeast corner of the province (Fig. 4.4). Most petroleum resources in Alberta, particularly in forested regions, are owned by the Crown. Private companies are able to extract these resources through tenure agreements with the government, administered by Alberta Energy. These tenure agreements,

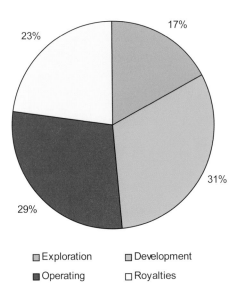

23%   17%

31%

29%

☐ Exploration   ☐ Development
■ Operating   ☐ Royalties

1.3   2.2

7.2

☐ Oil   ■ Gas   ☐ Tenure

Fig. 4.2. Petroleum industry expenditures in Alberta in 1999, by type. Source: CAPP, 2000.

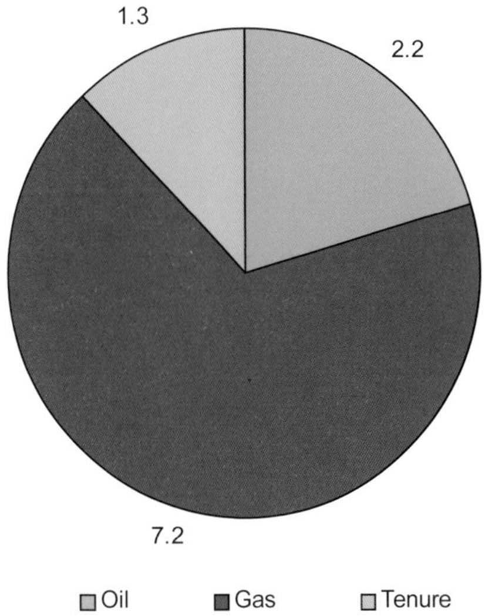

Fig. 4.3. Government revenue from oil and gas royalties and tenure agreements in Alberta in 2000/2001 ($ billions). Source: ARD, 2001.

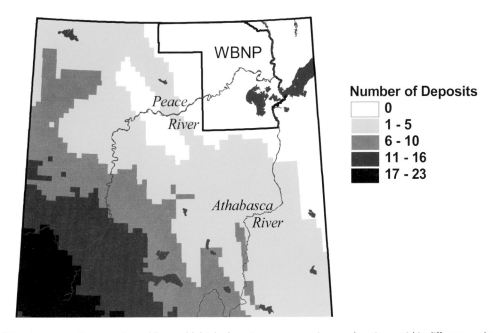

WBNP

Peace River

Athabasca River

Number of Deposits
☐ 0
☐ 1 - 5
▨ 6 - 10
▨ 11 - 16
■ 17 - 23

Fig. 4.4. Oil and gas deposits in northern Alberta. Multiple deposits are present in most locations, within different geological formations. Source: ERCB, 1992.

known as subsurface mineral rights, give companies the exclusive right to drill for and extract oil and gas in a specified area (GOA, 2000a, sec. 4). The rights may apply to all deposits within the specified area, or may be restricted to specific depths or type of product (oil or gas). Mineral rights do not include rights to surface access. Companies must separately obtain licences and approvals for surface activities such as seismic exploration, drilling, pipeline development, and road construction.

Mineral rights are generally awarded through an open competitive bidding process termed a "land sale". Companies may nominate parcels of land of interest to them for inclusion in a sale, but the rights ultimately go to the highest bidder. In

2000, the average price the government received for mineral rights was $275/ha (AE, 2001a).

By government regulation, parcels of land offered at land sales cannot exceed one township in size (GOA, 2000a, sec. 7). In practice, most offerings are substantially less than this maximum. Consequently, regional landscapes are typically composed of a patchwork of tenure holdings of many different companies (Fig. 4.5).

A key stipulation of petroleum tenure agreements is that companies must initiate exploratory drilling within a specified initial period (maximum = five years) (GOA, 2000a, sec. 14-16). If a site is proved to be productive then the agreement is continued indefinitely, otherwise the rights are returned to the Crown. In practice,

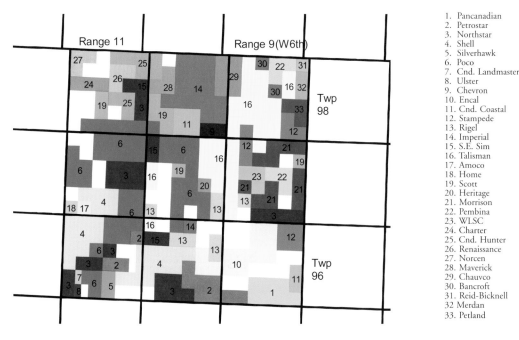

1. Pancanadian
2. Petrostar
3. Northstar
4. Shell
5. Silverhawk
6. Poco
7. Cnd. Landmaster
8. Ulster
9. Chevron
10. Encal
11. Cnd. Coastal
12. Stampede
13. Rigel
14. Imperial
15. S.E. Sim
16. Talisman
17. Amoco
18. Home
19. Scott
20. Heritage
21. Morrison
22. Pembina
23. WLSC
24. Charter
25. Cnd. Hunter
26. Renaissance
27. Norcen
28. Maverick
29. Chauvco
30. Bancroft
31. Reid-Bicknell
32. Merdan
33. Petland

Fig. 4.5. Typical distribution of oil and gas leases in northern Alberta. Company names are listed to the right of the figure (data current to 1997). (Map: Forest Watch Alberta)

companies often buy mineral rights for strategic reasons, but ultimately do not develop them. Also, many sites are drilled but found to be unproductive. As a result, over 75% of mineral rights revert back to the Crown for potential resale (AE, 1996: 18).

The Interdepartmental Crown Mineral Disposition Review Committee reviews proposed sales of mineral rights to identify potential impacts on the environment. However, *"The Committee does not conduct a detailed environmental assessment at this stage, because the posting and disposition of mineral rights, in and of itself, does not entail an environmental impact. The pertinent issue at the disposition stage is whether the posting is subject to Integrated Resource Plan land-use restrictions, or any other access restrictions. . ."* (AE, 1996: 18). In practice, mineral rights for sensitive wildlife habitat areas and protected areas are routinely posted for sale, with notification that certain restrictions on surface access will apply (e.g., AE, 2001b).

Achieving sustainable management of the forest as described in the *Alberta Forest Conservation Strategy* (AFCSSC, 1997) requires long-term regional planning that integrates all industrial users and limits cumulative impacts. The petroleum tenure system in Alberta, as currently structured, constitutes a significant barrier to achieving this goal. A fundamental problem is that the awarding of mineral rights is largely disconnected from regional planning. As a result, planning initiatives must contend with companies that already have tenure agreements in place, for which they have paid substantial sums of money. Ecosystem-based planning is further hindered by regulations that limit tenure agreements to small parcels of land and that force rapid exploitation of the resource. A comparison between the tenure system used for

the petroleum industry and that of the forest industry is provided in Table 4.2.

The recent *Special Places 2000* process provides an example of how the aforementioned factors can and do impede changes in land-use policy. First, because tenure agreements are small, most candidate protected areas involved many different oil and gas companies, resulting in negotiations that were slow and complex. Second, companies with tenure agreements in candidate protected area sites vigorously opposed any attempt to limit their activities in these sites, by virtue of their existing "rights". Finally, given ample financial resources and the dependence of the province on oil and gas revenues, the oil and gas industry was able to mount a powerful lobby effort. As a result of these factors, the *Special Places* process was completed with minimal impact on the oil and gas industry. The Foothills Ecoregion, where conventional oil and gas deposits are most abundant, remains 98.1% unprotected; 89% of parks in Alberta are less than 50 km^2 in size (i.e., largely accessible to companies via horizontal drilling); and oil and gas extraction in all new protected areas can continue under the provisions of tenure agreements in place prior to the site's establishment (AE, 1998; ACD, 2001). Future ecological forest management initiatives designed to integrate the petroleum and forestry industries and to limit cumulative industrial impacts will face similar challenges.

Seismic Exploration

Current Practices

Seismic (or geophysical) exploration is used to identify and map oil and gas deposits prior to drilling. The technique involves the production of sound waves at the surface, recording the waves

Table 4.2. Comparison of tenure regimes between the forest industry and the petroleum industry in Alberta.

	Forestry FMA Holders	Forestry Quota Holders	Petroleum Industry
Cost of tenure agreement	No cost	No cost	Tenure agreements sold by auction
Size of tenure agreement	Usually several thousand square kilometres	No fixed land holding; government determines where harvesting will occur	Up to one township in size (92 km²); most are much smaller
Forest management responsibilities	Defined in tenure contract; includes requirement for public involvement	Government has primary responsibility	No forest management responsibilities defined in tenure agreement
Company planning horizon	100 years	20 years	5-10 years
Term of agreement	20 years; renewable	20 years; renewable	Must drill in 2-5 years; indefinite continuation if productive
Public involvement	Public advisory committees	Government responsibility	Notify public of activities; respond to complaints

that are reflected from underlying features, and interpreting these reflections to produce a computer model of subsurface geological structures. Seismic exploration is conducted by specialized firms under contract to oil and gas producers and the findings normally become proprietary information of the producer. Some seismic companies will also conduct surveys in promising areas on speculation, and then sell the information to one or more producers at a later date.

Conventional seismic operations in forested regions involve the following steps. First, a long linear corridor, six to eight m in width, is cleared using a bulldozer (GOA, 1998, sec. 43; Fig. 4.6). Then truck-mounted drilling equipment is used to drill a series of holes at defined locations along the corridor for the placement of dynamite charges (the usual source of seismic sound waves). The dynamite charges are sequentially exploded and the reflected sound waves are recorded at the surface using portable recording equipment. In the final step a computer is used to amalgamate the sequential recordings into a seamless cross-sectional view of the subsurface. A complete seismic survey of an area typically involves a series of seismic lines running parallel to each other, usually at a distance of 400 m or more between lines.

Currently in Alberta, so-called *low-impact seismic* is becoming widely adopted for use in

Fig. 4.6. Conventional seismic operations in Alberta involve the creation of long linear access corridors using bulldozers. (Photos: R. Schneider, left; C. Wallis, right)

forested areas. *Low impact seismic* is characterized by seismic lines that are an average of five-metre wide and that follow a meandering course between dynamite shot points (LAD, 1999: 14). The intent is to reduce the loss of merchantable forest by avoiding valuable stands as much as possible. *Low impact seismic* also seeks to minimize disturbance of the soil and ground cover through the use of vehicles with low ground pressure (LAD, 1999: 14).

Although *low-impact seismic* represents an improvement over conventional seismic, the five-metre lines still result in a significant industrial footprint, and they still provide access into the forest. A further reduction in impact can be achieved through the use of so-called *enviro-drills*,

which are shot-hole drills mounted on specially designed all-terrain vehicles that require only two-metre corridors for access. New satellite positioning systems and inertial guidance systems (Schlumberger, 2001) enable shot points to be located without surveying, making it easier to cut meandering access routes for drilling equipment. The cost of using *enviro-drills* is currently higher than conventional methods (Table 4.3), but this cost differential should disappear once enviro-drills become widely available and operators become experienced using them. Furthermore, damage fees that must be paid to forest companies for loss of timber are reduced when *enviro-drills* are used, offsetting the cost of their use.

Vehicle access routes can be eliminated en-

Table 4.3. Relative cost of various seismic techniques in northern Alberta in 2000.

Technique	Cost per metre[1]
Truck-mounted drills	$3-5
Enviro-drills	$10-14
Heli-drills	$40 and up[2]

[1]Estimates provided by Western Geco, Calgary, AB.
[2]Cost is highly dependent on flying distance and terrain.

tirely by using heli-portable drills and recording equipment. However, 1.5-m hand-cut lines are still required to enable workers to lay down recording equipment. Although equipment is lowered to shot-hole sites by cable, helicopter landing sites must be available at regular intervals for safety reasons. More often than not, natural or industrial clearings are available for this purpose. Currently, *enviro-drills* and heli-portable drills are mostly being used in restricted areas, primarily along the East Slopes.

The seismic techniques described above provide a series of cross-sectional views of the earth — one slice for each seismic line. Advances in computer modelling have also made it possible to combine individual cross-sectional views into a full three-dimensional representation of the subsurface. However, to be used for 3D, seismic lines need to laid out in a grid pattern and at a closer spacing than for conventional 2D seismic. The use of 3-D techniques in Alberta is increasing, particularly for the steam extraction of in-situ oil sands deposits and for recovering residual oil from old reservoirs of conventional oil.

Ecological Impacts

In fiscal year 1999, the most recent year for which data are available, 101,000 km of seismic lines were approved in the Green Zone. Of these, 71,000 km involved new cutlines, and 30,000 km involved existing cutlines (Alberta Environment, unpublished data). The total length of seismic lines approved in the Green Zone is now over 1.5 *million* km (ECA, 1979: 28; AEP, 1998: 75).

Given conservative estimates of line widths, the area of forest harvested by seismic operations in the Green Zone from the start of operations in the 1950s to 1976 was 234,700 ha (ECA, 1979: 28). This compares with a harvest of 255,692 ha by the forest industry in the same region from 1956 to 1976 (ECA, 1979: 28). Because only a fraction of the wood from seismic operations is salvaged (being of the wrong species or age class, or impractical to haul out), the impact of seismic is largely additive to that of the forest industry.

In recent years the rate of harvesting by the forest industry has increased substantially, but so has the rate of seismic exploration. Consequently, the proportional impact of both industries is still similar. For example, on the Weyerhaeuser Edson FMA the annual average harvest from 1997 to 2001 was 1400 ha by the forest industry and 1083 ha by the petroleum industry (Varty, 2001). On the Alpac FMA the current rate of harvest is 16,000 ha/year by the forest industry and 11,000 ha/year by the petroleum industry (Pope, 2001).

A study in northeast Alberta has demonstrated that only 11.9% of seismic lines older than 20 years (n=62) were sufficiently regenerated to meet Alberta Forest Regeneration Survey Standards (MacFarlane, 1999). Similar rates of failure of forest regeneration have been described in the East Slopes (Revel et al., 1984). A combination of several factors is likely responsible for the observed failure in regeneration, including bulldozer damage to root systems, competition by grass species, ongoing disturbance by all-terrain vehicles and snowmobiles, and insufficient light penetration (Revel et al., 1984; MacFarlane, 1999).

Because regeneration is inadequate, seismic activities result in a progressive loss of mature forest and alteration of forest structure. Given the high rates of seismic activity in the Green Zone, the cumulative loss of habitat is substantial. These direct losses are magnified by the avoidance of habitat in the vicinity of seismic lines by some species, such as caribou (Dyer et al., 2001). Habitat effectiveness is further reduced by the extensive fragmentation of forest stands that results from seismic activity (Fig. 4.7).

Fragmentation reduces the abundance of large contiguous patches of forest that are required by forest-interior species (Bender et al.,

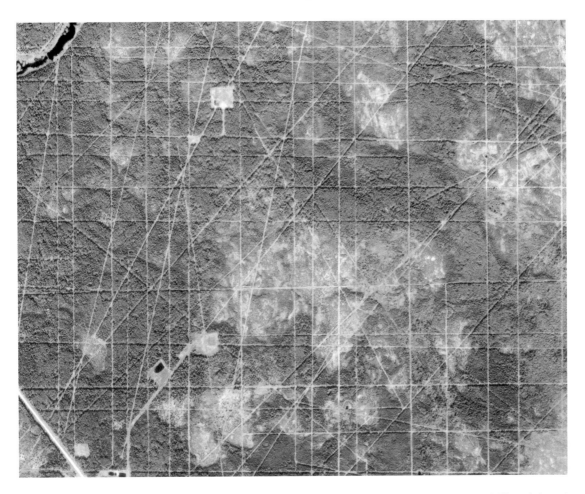

Fig. 4.7. Aerial photo illustrating the high density of seismic lines (white lines) present in many parts of Alberta's boreal forest (Twp 107, Rge 9, W6th; dimension of photo = 2.4 x 3 km; taken in 1992). (Air Photo Services, Alberta Sustainable Resource Development)

1998), and increases reproductive failure in birds due to nest predation and cowbird parasitism (Burke and Nol, 2000).

Seismic activities have several additional ecological impacts:

1. Increased access. Seismic lines provide access routes into the forest for all-terrain vehicles, snowmobiles, and off-road trucks. This leads to increased hunting and poaching and can have significant adverse effects on soil and vegetation, effectively delaying regeneration (CAPP, 1999a: E-3).

2. Damage to aquatic systems. Deleterious impacts include increased stream sedimentation, bank erosion, barriers to fish passage, destruction of aquatic habitats, and alteration of drainage patterns (CAPP, 1999a: D-13).

3. Alteration in predator-prey interactions. Wolves are able to move faster along seismic lines than in the forest and this has been associated with increased predation pressure on caribou (James, 1999).

4. Damage to soil. Deleterious impacts include compaction and mixing of soil horizons by heavy equipment, erosion, and soil cratering from shot holes that are not properly filled (CAPP, 1999a: F-3).

5. Disturbance of wildlife. Clearing operations and dynamite explosions can disturb wildlife, particularly during nesting and calving periods (CAPP, 1999a: D-3). Repeated disturbances can result in significant energy losses by increasing movement rates during the winter when food supplies are limited (Bradshaw, et al., 1998).

6. Introduction of aggressive weed species into the forest (CAPP, 1999a: F-15).

Regulatory Framework

Oil and gas exploration is generally not permitted in East Slope Prime Protection lands or protected areas (AE, 1996: 16). However, "grandfathering" clauses permit exploration when required to develop mineral rights that were acquired prior to an area being designated as protected (AE, 1996: 16).

To conduct a seismic program a company must obtain an *Exploration Approval*, administered by Alberta Sustainable Resource Development (GOA, 1998, sec. 9). Applications pertaining to public land must be accompanied by *Geophysical Field Report*, which provides site-specific details as to how environmental issues will be addressed during the clearing, operating, and reclamation phases of the geophysical program (LAD, 1999: 3). A company does not need to hold mineral rights for an area to obtain an *Exploration Approval.*

The intent of the *Geophysical Field Report* is to have the applicants outline how they plan to meet the relevant environmental standards, instead of having the government address these details in the form of approval conditions (LAD, 1999: 3). The submitted application is reviewed by various government departments, including Lands and Forest Service, Fish and Wildlife, and Land Administration, to check for deficiencies. By law, the government must provide a response within ten working days (GOA, 1998, sec. 11).

The *Geophysical Field Report* includes the following elements (LAD, 1999: 6-16):

1. Description of ground conditions. It is expected that operations in northern muskegs will be done under frozen ground conditions.

2. Identification of areas of concern (e.g.,

parks, critical wildlife zones, and areas subject to Integrated Resource Plans). These areas generally have special operating rules.

3. Watercourse crossings. All crossings must be identified and measures for mitigating environmental concerns must be explained.

4. Buffer zones. Buffers, where operating restrictions apply, are required around aquatic features (10-45 m) and designated wildlife protection corridors (50-100 m).

5. Water bodies. Restrictions on drilling and use of dynamite may apply, depending on the type of water body.

6. Existing seismic lines. Existing lines must be used if they are parallel and within 400 m, unless justification for an exemption can be made. In practice, successive seismic surveys often run in different directions, resulting in high local densities of lines (Fig. 4.7).

7. Proposed access. Access to the survey site should normally be achieved using existing roads, trails, and seismic lines.

8. Line type and width. *Low impact seismic* is now generally required in areas of merchantable forest. Conventional seismic remains acceptable in muskeg areas.

9. Timber management. Plans should include measures to minimize losses of merchantable timber. Salvage of timber may be required for conventional seismic programs, but *low impact seismic* programs are exempt.

After one year the survey site is inspected to ensure that environmental regulations were followed. If the site is acceptable a *Letter of Clearance* is issued, absolving the company of any further responsibility for the site. Companies are not required to reforest the site, though some sort of

vegetation cover must be present to prevent erosion (LAD, 2000).

From the perspective of sustainable forest management, the regulatory framework governing seismic activities is fundamentally deficient in two respects. First, given that *Geophysical Field Reports* must be reviewed by multiple government departments (that are typically short-staffed) it is inconceivable that a thorough environmental review can be accomplished within the allotted ten-day period. As observed by the Environmental Council of Alberta (1979: 27),

> *The emphasis on haste that the [petroleum] industry has adopted over the years seems to have been accepted by the government. This is not conducive to good planning, which requires time to evaluate a proposed program or development.*

A second deficiency of the regulatory framework is that it is focussed on local and short-term issues, and not on sustainability of the forest as a whole. In particular, there are no regulations that limit the overall rate of harvest or require that the forest be regenerated. Neither is there any requirement that seismic activities be integrated with the long-term harvest plans of forestry companies that share the same land base. In fact, forestry companies have no control over exploration activities that occur on the land base they are charged with managing. As a consequence, efforts by forestry companies to achieve ecological forest management targets are critically hindered.

In addition to the general deficiencies described above there are also problems with individual regulations. However, a comprehensive review of the adequacy of the individual regulations governing seismic activities is beyond the scope of this book.

Drilling and Production

Current Practices

As with seismic exploration, most drilling is conducted by specialized companies that market their services to producers (PCF, 1999: 39). However, a few of the larger producers still own and operate their own drilling rigs. The cost of drilling is a function of depth, ranging from about $100,000 for a shallow well (450 m) on the prairies to more than a million dollars for a deep well (4000 m) in the foothills (PCF, 1996: 3).

The first step in drilling is the construction of an access road capable of handling large volumes of heavy truck traffic. Drilling rigs are large complex structures that are designed to be disassembled and moved from site to site (Fig. 4.8). Transport of a large rig can involve up to 50 semi-trailer trucks (PCF, 1999: 39). Additional truck traffic is generated by the transport of workers and supplies, including fuel, water, food, specialty chemicals, and drilling mud. It is also necessary to clear an area at the drilling site for the assembly of the rig and to facilitate the local movement of workers and equipment. Well site clearings of one hectare are typical in forested regions in Alberta (LAD, 2001: 10).

Drilling involves about 75 workers in total per typical well, working in round-the-clock shifts, seven days a week (PCF, 1999: 42). Though many technological refinements have been made in recent years, the drilling process is still based on the movement of a rotating bit through rock. A fluid called mud lubricates the bit and removes rock cuttings, stabilizes the hole, and controls the pressure in the wellbore. The mud is a suspension of chemicals and minerals in water or oil.

Once the oil or gas reservoir is reached, the well casing is cemented in place and a well head is installed to regulate the flow of product. Gas usually flows under its own pressure, though a compressor may be required to boost the pressure for pipeline transport. The extraction of crude oil is more complicated, and in most cases some form of pumping is required. Many wells also require "stimulation", by physical or chemical means, so that oil can move more easily through pores or fractures in the reservoir. A common method of stimulation involves the injection of concentrated acids under pressure into the rock formation (PCF, 1999: 48).

Fig. 4.8. Conventional oil drilling rig and support equipment. (Photo: Al-Pac)

The primary recovery techniques described above are able to recover an average of only 20% of the oil in a reservoir (PCF, 1999: 49). Therefore, a variety of enhanced recovery techniques are generally utilized, the nature of which is determined by the type of oil involved. For light oil (i.e., low density and viscosity), the most common enhanced recovery technique is infill drilling, which simply means drilling more wells into the same reservoir so that the oil does not have to travel as far to reach a wellbore. New directional drilling techniques permit multiple wells to be drilled from a common drilling pad, reducing the environmental impact of infill drilling.

Other enhanced recovery techniques involve the injection of water or natural gas to maintain reservoir pressure and push the oil out of the rock (PCF, 1999: 49). More advanced techniques include the injection of natural gas liquids, such as propane, into the reservoir to dissolve into the oil and reduce its viscosity, thereby aiding its release from the rock. Even with enhanced recovery techniques, the average recovery for light oil is not much more than 30% (PCF, 1999: 49).

In heavy oil fields and in-situ oil sands (Fig. 2.17), enhanced recovery generally involves the application of heat. Without heat the oil is simply too thick to be extracted. The most common technique is called steam-assisted gravity drainage which uses parallel pairs of horizontal wells for steam injection and oil recovery (PCF, 1999: 49). Steam recovery is far more intensive than conventional oil extraction because it involves batteries of closely spaced wells, it requires large quantities of water and power for generating steam, and it makes extensive use of 3D seismic surveys (AEC, 1999).

The oil sands deposits in an area of approximately 37 townships north of Fort McMurray

(Fig. 2.17) are sufficiently close to the surface to be directly mined. Discussion of oil sands mining is beyond the scope of this book; however, suffice it to say that mining represents the most intensive and environmentally damaging method of oil extraction in the province.

Once a well has been brought into production it is generally tied into a pipeline system to transport the product to processing plants of various types. The construction of pipelines involves further clearing of linear corridors to provide access, and trenching for the laying of pipe. Regular ground or aerial patrols of pipelines are required to ensure that pipeline integrity is continually maintained. Consequently, forest regrowth along pipeline right-of-ways is prevented for the life of the pipeline through mechanical or chemical means (CAPP, 1999b: E-14).

Whereas oil is generally transported in raw form to refineries near major population centres for processing, most processing of natural gas is done at gas plants located near production areas (PCF, 1999: 60). Consequently, a large proportion of the 684 gas plants in Alberta are located within forested areas. The processing of gas involves the separation of natural gas (methane) from the raw gas stream which includes heavier hydrocarbons (e.g., ethane and propane), water vapour, and other gases. When hydrogen sulphide is present (sour gas), it is also removed, usually at larger facilities.

In the past, all-weather roads to well sites had to be maintained to provide access for well monitoring, maintenance, and repairs. However, through advances in automation and telemetry, it is now possible to monitor wells remotely (PCF, 1996: 6). Consequently, gas wells, which require minimal maintenance, can now be serviced by helicopter, and access roads can be removed

(BCC, 2001: 25). However, this is not yet a common practice. Because oil wells generally have pumps and other equipment that require regular maintenance, remote service of oil wells is difficult and is not yet being implemented.

The typical lifespan of a well is about 25 years, though many wells produce for longer periods. If a producing well is no longer economical to operate the well bore is plugged with cement and the site is reclaimed. A similar process is followed for new wells that are found to be dry (i.e., not capable of producing commercial quantities of oil or gas).

Ecological Impacts

As with seismic lines, it is not the impact of individual wells that is of primary concern, but the cumulative impact of all wells. In 2000 alone, 11,898 new wells were drilled in Alberta (AE, 2001c). The cumulative area of existing wells in the Boreal Forest Natural Region, as of 1997, has been estimated to be over 886 km^2 (AEP, 1998: 75). Furthermore, each well has a road leading to it and frequently a pipeline right-of-way leading away from it (Fig. 4.9).

The clearing of trees associated with the construction of well sites, access roads, and pipelines is associated with the same list of ecological impacts described for seismic lines (CAPP, 1999c: D-3). Although the total amount of clearing is less than that associated with seismic exploration, the local impact is substantially greater. For example, caribou avoid wells to a distance of 1000 m, which is four times the avoidance distance for seismic lines (Dyer et al., 2001). Roads provide faster access for more types of vehicles and cause more erosion and greater disruption of drainage patterns. Finally, well sites, roads, and pipeline right-of-ways are essentially permanent features

of the landscape, given their prolonged use and slow regeneration after decommissioning.

In addition to general landscape impacts associated with deforestation, there are ecological impacts related to the contamination of soil and water. Such contamination reduces soil and water quality. Furthermore, many contaminants are classified as hazardous and may be toxic or carcinogenic (AEUB, 1996: App. 7.4). The major types of soil and water contaminants are (AEUB, 1996: App. 7.4):

- subsurface products including hydrocarbons, saline water, and heavy metals;
- drilling mud and associated chemicals and minerals;
- concentrated acids used for well stimulation and other "process chemicals";
- industrial fluids (solvents, fuel, lubricants); and
- sewage and garbage.

Contamination of soil, surface water, and groundwater with the aforementioned products occurs in a variety of ways, including (CAPP, 1999c: sec. E):

- oilfield waste disposal by spreading on land and roads (both are officially condoned practices, with minimal oversight: AEUB, 1996: sec. 16.2);
- underground leakage during drilling due to faulty well casings;
- spills and continuous leaks during operations;
- faulty storage structures;
- improper transport and disposal of wastes; and
- pipeline failures.

Drilling and production are also associated with reductions in air quality through the release of various of gaseous emissions. Some of these

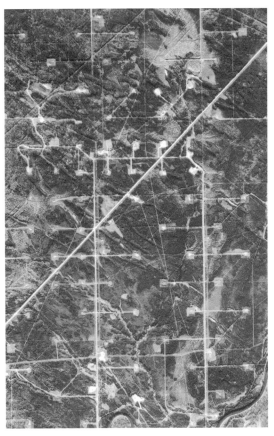

Fig. 4.9a. Aerial photograph illustrating well sites (pale squares), access roads (thick lines), and seismic lines (Twp 51, Rge 9, W5th; dimension = 0.8 x 1.2 km; taken 1992). (Photo: Air Photo Services, Alberta Sustainable Resource Development)

Fig. 4.9b. Aerial photograph illustrating the distribution of well sites (pale squares), and access roads at smaller scale (Twp 48, Rge 9, W5th; dimension = 4.7 x 7.3 km; taken 1994). (Photo: Air Photo Services, Alberta Sustainable Resource Development)

emissions, such as benzene and carbon monoxide, are directly toxic (CAPP, 1999c: C-35). Others, such as sulphur dioxide and nitrogen dioxide, are responsible for acid rain deposition (Schindler, 1998). Methane and carbon dioxide are important greenhouse gases. Alberta has the highest greenhouse gas emissions in Canada, largely as a consequence of energy-sector activities (EC, 1997). Not surprisingly, public concerns about petroleum industry emissions are very high, particularly among rural residents (Marr-Laing and Severson-Baker, 1999).

Sources of gaseous emissions include the following (CAPP, 1999c: Sec. C):

- leaking and flaring of gas produced as a byproduct of oil production (Fig. 4.10);
- well blowouts;
- glycol dehydrators, used to remove water

Fig. 4.10. Flaring of gas. (Photo: Canadian Parks and Wilderness Society - Edmonton)

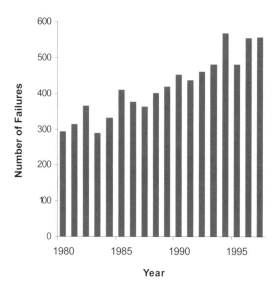

Fig. 4.11. Number of oil and gas pipeline failures in Alberta, 1980-1997. Source: AEUB, 1998.

vapour from the gas stream (primary source of benzene emissions);
- test flaring of new gas wells;
- flaring of gas and sulphur recovery at gas processing plants;
- inadequate storage and handling facilities;
- oil spills and leaks and disposal of oil wastes via spreading on land and roads; and
- pipeline failures (Fig. 4.11).

A final issue of note is the diversion and use of freshwater for enhanced oil recovery. This includes pumping water into reservoirs to maintain reservoir pressure and the generation of steam for steam-assisted gravity drainage. Although water is recycled as much as possible, both techniques involve large net inputs of freshwater over time. In 2001, Alberta Environment gave oil and gas companies permission to inject 230 billion litres of freshwater down well bores — enough water to supply the city of Red Deer for 25 years (Nikiforuk, 2002). The use of fresh groundwater by the petroleum sector is currently exceeded only by municipalities (Table 4.4). Concern has been expressed that this rate of use of freshwater, which

Table. 4.4. Annual allocation of fresh ground-water in Alberta in 2001.

Sector	Cubic Metres	Percent
Municipalities	48,365,779	29.5
Oil recovery	42,604,001	26.0
Agriculture	28,089,236	17.1
Commercial	23,634,898	14.4
Fish management	9,386,905	5.7
Other industrial	5,414,923	3.3
Recreation	4,957,436	3.0
Other	1,552,247	0.1
Total	164,005,425	100.0

Source: Alberta Government, cited in Nikiforuk, 2002.

is set to increase as the industry expands, will jeopardize the provincial supply of freshwater required for other human needs (Marr-Laing and Severson-Baker, 1999; Nikiforuk, 2002).

Regulatory Framework

Subsurface mineral rights do not provide petroleum companies with the right to conduct activities on the surface. On public lands, companies must separately obtain a *Mineral Surface Lease* and related agreements in order to drill wells and construct roads and pipelines (GOA, 2000b, sec. 76). These agreements are administered by Alberta Sustainable Resource Development. As with seismic exploration, drilling and production are not permitted in certain areas, such as protected areas, unless grandfathering clauses exist.

Pursuant to subsection 7(2) of the *Dispositions and Fees Regulation* (GOA, 2000b), forestry companies that hold tenure rights in an area must provide written consent before a *Mineral Surface Lease* can be issued. In practice, this legal avenue for managing the activities of petroleum companies has never been exercised by forestry companies. Presumably, this is because the government retains contractual rights to remove lands from forest management areas as required for industrial purposes.

Applications for a *Mineral Surface Lease* must be accompanied by an *Environmental Field Report* (LAD, 2001) in which applicants identify environmental issues and describe acceptable methods for addressing them. Applications are reviewed by various government departments and, unless deficiencies are noted, approvals are provided within 15 working days (Graham, 2001). The key elements of the *Environmental Field Report* are:

- identification of "areas of concern", where special management rules apply;
- timber salvage;
- well site development;
- access road construction (route, size, type); and
- watercourse crossings.

Before drilling can proceed a company must also obtain a well licence from the Alberta Energy and Utilities Board. The role of the Board is to ensure that energy resources are developed in a responsible and efficient manner. One of the ways it does this is by regulating the spacing of wells. Normally, oil wells are spaced at one per quarter section of land and gas wells at one per section, unless it can be shown that additional wells are necessary "*to provide capacity to drain the pool at a reasonable rate*" (GOA, 2001, sec. 4.020 and 4.040).

For conventional wells on public land the Energy and Utilities Board generally accepts that all surface issues have been resolved through the *Mineral Surface Lease* process (AE, 1996: 19). Consequently, routine applications are normally approved in less than five working days (CAPP, 1999c: B-7). Intensive steam-assisted gravity drainage projects, oil sands mines, and other large projects generally require an Environmental Impact Assessment prior to approval. However, none of the proposed oil sands projects (totaling tens of billions of dollars) have been declined, in spite of the fact that defined limits on regional cumulative impacts do not exist.

The Energy and Utilities Board is also responsible for ongoing regulation of active wells, including the regulation of emissions and handling of wastes. As scientific evidence of the harmful effects of pollution mounts, there is growing concern that the existing regulatory framework governing operations is inadequate (Marr-Laing and Severson-Baker, 1999: 1). There is additional concern that existing regulations are not being effectively enforced, as a consequence of recent government downsizing (Marr-Laing and Severson-Baker, 1999: 1). The most serious deficiencies include unacceptable levels of gas venting and flaring, unacceptable levels of benzene release from gas plants, inadequate standards for the handling of oil field wastes, and inadequate regulation of groundwater resources. These issues are reviewed in detail in a recent paper by the Pembina Institute (Marr-Laing and Severson-Baker, 1999).

The decommissioning and reclamation of well sites is administered by the Alberta Energy and Utilities Board and by Sustainable Resource Development. The objective of the reclamation process is to "*return the specified land to an equivalent land capability*" (GOA, 1999: sec. 2). This is narrowly interpreted to mean that the site must be capable of growing trees, but restoration of the original forest is not required. Consequently, well sites are normally reseeded to grass (LAD, 2001: 10). Other reclamation requirements include the removal of contaminants, restoration of the original topography, and restoration of soil conditions (AEP, 1999). Once reclamation has been completed the company is awarded a Reclamation Certificate, absolving it of further responsibility for the site. In the Green Area, government inspection of reclaimed sites is not mandatory, but instead is based on an audit system (GOA, 1999: sec. 6.2).

A more detailed review of specific regulations pertaining to drilling and production is beyond the scope of this book. However, it is important to note that the same general deficiencies I described for seismic exploration apply to the regulation of oil and gas wells. Even though the construction of oil and gas wells and associated infrastructure have a tremendous impact on the structure and integrity of the forest, there are no regulatory or policy limits on the annual rate of forest clearing, no requirements for reforestation, no thresholds for cumulative impacts, and no requirements for integrated long-term planning with the forest industry intended to maintain forest sustainability. Instead, the regulatory framework is focussed on mitigating industrial activities on a case by case basis with minimal review and no recognition that the forest has a finite capacity to meet the needs of multiple industrial users.

Literature Cited

ACD (**Alberta Community Development**). 2001. Parks and protected areas GIS map, revised Aug. 28, 2001 (Available at: www.gov.ab.ca/env/parks/lrm/index.html)

AE (**Alberta Energy**). 1996. Environmental regulation of natural gas development in Alberta, Canada. Alberta Energy, Edmonton, AB.

AE (**Alberta Energy**). 1998. Special Places Program: interim protection measures, boreal forest natural region. IL 98 –39. (Available at: www.energy.gov.ab.ca)

AE (**Alberta Energy**). 2001a. Summary of annual public offering of Crown petroleum and natural gas rights - leases and licences. Department of Energy, Edmonton, AB. (Available at: www.energy.gov.ab.ca)

AE (**Alberta Energy**). 2001b. Public offering of Crown petroleum and natural gas rights: Sept. 19, 2001. Department of Energy, Edmonton, AB. (Available at: www.energy.gov.ab.ca)

AE (**Alberta Energy**). 2001c. Industry activity reports: June, 2001. Department of Energy, Edmonton, AB. (Available at: www.energy.gov.ab.ca)

AEC (**Alberta Energy Company**). 1999. Foster Creek in situ oil sands project: environmental impact assessment. Alberta Energy Company, Calgary, AB.

AEP (**Alberta Environmental Protection**). 1998. The

Boreal Forest Natural Region of Alberta. Alberta Environmental Protection, Edmonton, AB.

AEP (**Alberta Environmental Protection**). 1999. Reclamation certification process for wellsites: IL 99-4. Alberta Environmental Protection, Edmonton, AB. (Available at: www3.gov.ab.ca/env/info/infocentre/index.cfm)

AEUB (**Alberta Energy and Utilities Board**). 1996. Guide 58: Oilfield waste management requirements for the upstream petroleum industry. Alberta Energy and Utilities Board, Calgary, AB. (Available at: www.eub.gov.ab.ca)

AEUB (**Alberta Energy and Utilities Board**). 1998. Pipeline performance in Alberta 1980-1997. Alberta Energy and Utilities Board, Calgary, AB. (Available at: www.eub.gov.ab.ca)

AFCSSC (**Alberta Forest Conservation Strategy Steering Committee**). 1997. Alberta forest conservation strategy. Alberta Environmental Protection, Edmonton, AB. (Available at: www.borealcentre.ca/reports/reports.html)

ARD (**Alberta Resource Development**). 2000. Alberta's energy industry: overview and economic impact. Alberta Resource Development, Edmonton, AB. (Available at: www.energy.gov.ab.ca)

ARD (**Alberta Resource Development**). 2001. Annual report: 2000/2001. Alberta Resource Development, Edmonton, AB. (Available at: www.energy.gov.ab.ca)

Bender, D. J., T. A. Contreras, and L. Fahrig. 1998. Habitat loss and population decline: a meta-analysis of the patch size effect. Ecology 79:517-533.

BCC (**Boreal Caribou Committee**). 2001. Strategic plan and industrial guidelines for boreal caribou ranges in northern Alberta. Boreal Caribou Committee, Edmonton, AB. (Available at: www.deer.rr.ualberta.ca/caribou/bcrp.htm)

Bradshaw, C. J. A., S. Boutin, and D. M. Hebert. 1998. Energetic implications of disturbance caused by petroleum exploration to woodland caribou. Can. J. Zool. 76:1319-1324.

Burke, D. and E. Nol. 2000. Landscape and fragment size effects on reproductive success of forest-breeding birds in Ontario. Ecol. Applic. 10:1749-1761.

CAPP (**Canadian Association of Petroleum Producers**). 1999a. Environmental operating practices for upstream petroleum operations: Alberta operations. Volume II: geophysics. Canadian Association of Petroleum Producers, Calgary, AB.

CAPP (**Canadian Association of Petroleum Producers**). 1999b. Environmental operating practices for upstream petroleum operations: Alberta operations. Volume V: pipelines. Canadian Association of Petroleum Producers, Calgary, AB.

CAPP (**Canadian Association of Petroleum Producers**). 1999c. Environmental operating practices for upstream petroleum operations: Alberta operations. Volume IV: production. Canadian Association of Petroleum Producers, Calgary, AB.

CAPP (**Canadian Association of Petroleum Producers**). 2000. Statistical handbook for Canada's upstream petroleum industry. Canadian Association of Petroleum Producers, Calgary, AB.

Dyer, S. J., J. P. O'Neill, S. M. Wasel, and S. Boutin. 2001. Avoidance of industrial development by woodland caribou. J. Wildl. Manage. 65:531-542.

EC (**Environment Canada**). 1997. Provincial emissions: 1997 greenhouse gas emission summary. Environment Canada (Available at: www.ec.gc.ca/pdb/ghg/Provem_e.cfm)

ECA (**Environment Council of Alberta**). 1979. The environmental effects of forestry operations in Alberta: report and recommendations. Environmental Council of Alberta, Edmonton, AB.

ERCB (**Energy Resources Conservation Board**). 1992. Report 92-A: Ultimate potential and supply of natural gas in Alberta. Energy Resources Conservation Board, Calgary, AB.

GOA (**Government of Alberta**). 1998. Exploration regulation, AR 214/98. Queen's Printer of Alberta, Edmonton, AB. (Available at: www.gov.ab.ca/qp/)

GOA (**Government of Alberta**). 1999. Conservation and reclamation regulation, AR 115/93 . Queen's Printer of Alberta, Edmonton, AB. (Available at: www.gov.ab.ca/qp/)

GOA (**Government of Alberta**). 2000a. Petroleum and natural gas tenure regulation, AR 263/97. Queen's Printer of Alberta, Edmonton, AB. (Available at: www.gov.ab.ca/qp/)

GOA (**Government of Alberta**). 2000b. Dispositions and fees regulation, AR 54/2000. Queen's Printer of Alberta, Edmonton, AB. (Available at: www.gov.ab.ca/qp/)

GOA (**Government of Alberta**). 2001. Oil and gas conservation regulations, AR 151/71. Queen's Printer of Alberta, Edmonton, AB. (Available at: www.gov.ab.ca/qp/)

Graham, G. 2001. Oil and gas activity on Alberta public lands. In: Oil and gas planning on forested lands in Alberta: overview of CIF-RMS technical session, March 23, 2001. Canadian Institute of Forestry, Edmonton, AB.

Alternative Futures

James, A. R. 1999. Effects of industrial development on the predator-prey relationship between wolves and caribou in northwestern Alberta. Ph.D. Thesis, University of Alberta, Edmonton, AB.

LAD (Land Administration Division). 1999. Guidelines for the submission of the Geophysical Field Report. Land Administration Division, Edmonton, AB. (Available at: www3.gov.ab.ca/srd/land/lad/)

LAD (Land Administration Division). 2000. Geophysical site condition report. Land Administration Division, Edmonton, AB. (Available at: www3.gov.ab.ca/srd/land/lad/)

LAD (Land Administration Division). 2001. Instructions for the submission of the Environmental Field Report with applications for dispositions under the Public Lands Act. Land Administration Division, Edmonton, AB. (Available at: www3.gov.ab.ca/srd/land/lad/)

MacFarlane, A. 1999. Revegetation of wellsites and seismic lines in the boreal forest. University of Alberta, Honors thesis, Edmonton, AB. (Available at: www.borealcentre.ca/reports/reports.html)

Marr-Laing, T. and C. Severson-Baker. 1999. Beyond ecoterrorism: the deeper issues affecting Alberta's oilpatch. Pembina Institute, Drayton Valley, AB. (Available at: www.pembina.org)

Nikiforuk, A. 2002. Use of groundwater by the oil and gas industry. National Post, July 1, 2002: 46.

NRC (Natural Resources Canada). 1995. Canadian petroleum industry — 1994 monitoring report. Natural Resources Canada, Ottawa, ON.

PCF (Petroleum Communication Foundation). 1996. Technology for exploration and production. Petroleum Communication Foundation, Calgary, AB.

PCF (Petroleum Communication Foundation). 1999. Our petroleum challenge: exploring Canada's oil and gas industry. Petroleum Communication Foundation, Calgary, AB.

PCF (Petroleum Communication Foundation). 2000. Petroleum industry fast facts: Alberta. Petroleum Communication Foundation, Calgary, AB. (Available at: www.pcf.ab.ca)

Pope, D. 2001. Integrated landscape management on the Alpac FMA. In: Oil and gas planning on forested lands in Alberta: overview of CIF-RMS technical session, March 23, 2001. Canadian Institute of Forestry, Edmonton, AB.

Revel, R. D., T. D. Dougherty, and D. J. Downing. 1984. Forest Growth and Regeneration Along Seismic Lines.

University of Calgary Press, Calgary, AB.

Schindler, D. 1998. A dim future for boreal waters and landscapes. BioScience 48:157-164.

Schlumberger. 2001. NavPac. Web page downloaded Sept. 2001 at: www.slb.com/Hub/brochure/index.cfm?b=connect/geophysics/Navpac&id=id12241

SC (Statistics Canada). 2002. Query of the CANSIM II database: Table 281-0024 - Employment (SEPH), unadjusted for seasonal variation, by type of employee for selected industries, 2001. Statistics Canada, Ottawa, ON. (Available at: cansim2.statcan.ca/)

Varty, T. 2001. Basic concerns from a forest industry perspective. In: Oil and gas planning on forested lands in Alberta: overview of CIF-RMS technical session, March 23, 2001. Canadian Institute of Forestry, Edmonton, AB.

5. Cumulative Impacts

Integrated Resource Management in Alberta

With the exception of the northeast, where petroleum deposits are absent and forest productivity is low, most of Alberta's boreal forest is subject to the overlapping activities of multiple industrial operators (Fig. 5.1). For example, a given area might have an FMA holder, several forestry quota holders, and many petroleum companies, all operating concurrently and independently.

Although attempts at integrated resource management have been made in Alberta since the 1970s, the reality is that different industrial sectors continue to be managed by different government agencies utilizing different policy instruments (Kennett, 2002). If there is any unifying feature among these agencies it is a common mandate for economic growth (e.g., ARD, 2001: 43). In spite of provincial commitments to maintain forest integrity (e.g., AEP, 1998a), environmental protection continues to be handled through piecemeal regulations focussed on mitigating the local short-term effects of individual industrial activities. Strategies for achieving long-term ecological objectives at the regional scale, including limits on cumulative industrial impacts, have yet to be implemented.

In the absence of an integrated planning framework, the activities of resource companies operating on the same land base are largely additive. In addition, fire continues

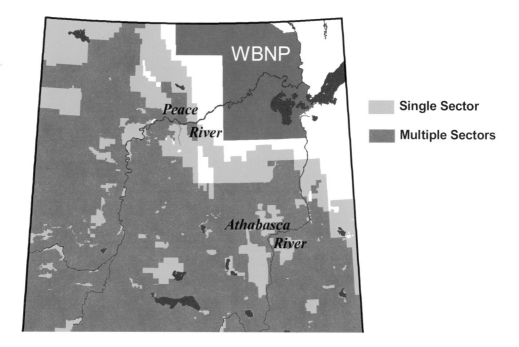

Fig. 5.1. Area of northern Alberta subject to overlapping industrial activities. Sectors include agriculture (White Zone), forestry (FMA boundaries), and petroleum (extent of deposits). (Map: Forest Watch Alberta)

to be a significant source of disturbance, in spite of the efforts of the Forest Protection Branch (see Chapter 6).

Although the forest has a natural tendency to regenerate after being disturbed, the rate of regeneration varies widely, depending on the type of disturbance. For example, regeneration after fire and clearcutting is usually well advanced within 10 years. Other disturbances such as cutblock landings (where trees are stored prior to hauling) and seismic lines may take decades to regenerate (Osko and MacFarlane, 2001). Roads, well sites, and pipelines represent long-term deletions from the forest.

The lag in regeneration following many types of industrial disturbance has already resulted in observable changes to the structure of the forest,

relative to its natural state (AEP, 1998b). The amount of additional change that will occur in the future will depend on the interplay between the rate of new disturbance and the rate of regeneration. Given the current high rates of disturbance over most of the north, and observed lags in regeneration, it appears certain that profound changes in forest structure will continue to occur unless changes are made to the way the forest is managed.

A new integrated resource management initiative began in 1999 (AE, 2000) that could address many of the issues outlined here. The process is still in its formative stage, so it is too early to determine the eventual outcome. But one thing is clear — to succeed, the new process must be fundamentally different from the various processes that preceded it. Earlier integrated resource management initiatives had the following deficiencies (Kennett, 2002):

- vague short-term objectives emphasizing multiple use instead of a long-term vision for the entire forest that includes clear ecological objectives;
- failure to accept that the forest has finite limits that are now being reached, and that thresholds on cumulative industrial impacts need to be instituted;
- reliance on the existing organizational and policy framework instead of undertaking structural reform designed to provide the basis for truly integrated forest management;
- failure to entrench the integrated management process in law and provide it with sufficient power to overcome sectoral resistance;
- failure to establish direct links between planning and decision-making (e.g., for dispositions, project review, and regulatory decisions);
- rigid policy of honouring existing commitments instead of seeking innovative solutions for progress;
- failure to incorporate meaningful public input and public values into the planning process; and
- insufficient application of political commitment and will to ensure success.

The Future Forest

To illustrate the future state of the forest under current management policies I present here a case study involving the FMA of Alberta-Pacific Forest Industries (Al-Pac). The data are from a recent cumulative impacts study conducted by Schneider et al. (2002) using a computer model called *ALCES®* (Alberta Landscape Cumulative Effects Simulator). *ALCES* was developed over a period of seven years by Dr. Brad Stelfox for the purpose of tracking cumulative changes in forest structure arising from human and natural disturbances under alternative management scenarios.

Study Area

The study area was the Al-Pac FMA, encompassing 59,054 km^2 in northeast Alberta (Fig. 5.2). The area has minimal topographic relief, with the exception of a few scattered hill systems. Most of the area is within the Central Mixedwood Natural Subregion, with some representation of the Boreal Highlands Natural Subregion (AEP, 1994a).

The study area contains 23,842 km^2 of potentially merchantable forest and is underlain by extensive oil and gas deposits. The oil deposits

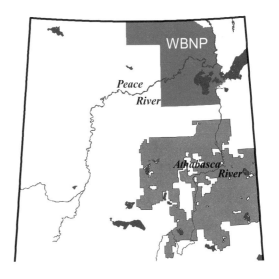

Fig. 5.2. Location of the Al-Pac FMA (in red).

include conventional liquid oil, heavy oil (low viscosity), and oil sands (a mixture of sand and semi-solid oil). In an area of approximately 37 townships the oil sands are sufficiently close to the surface to be extracted using surface mines. The remaining deeper oil sands deposits must be extracted through special well systems that utilize steam to heat the oil and mobilize it.

Industrial activity within the study area was minimal in the first half of the 20th century (Wetherell and Kmet, 2000), but expanded rapidly thereafter. Small-scale forestry operations producing dimensional lumber and conventional oil and gas operations were active first. In 1967 the first full-scale commercial oil sands mine went into operation, ushering in a period of rapid growth of the petroleum sector. In 1990 the Al-Pac Forest Management Agreement was signed, and the company's $1.3 billion pulp mill went into operation in 1993. The forestry sector currently clears a total of 16,000 ha/year on the study area, compared with 11,000 ha/year for the petroleum sector (Pope, 2001).

GIS map overlays provided by Al-Pac were used to quantify the industrial footprint existing in the study area in 2002 (Table 5.1). Included in the industrial footprint were all areas of the forest land base currently in a non-forest state as a result of industrial activity. Forestry cutblocks were not included in the tally because they are immediately regenerated to forest; however, in-block haul roads and landings (which experience delayed regeneration) were included. These data were used to define the initial state of the forest for the *ALCES* model runs.

The ALCES Model

ALCES was developed for the purpose of tracking industrial footprints and ecological processes

under alternative management scenarios. To facilitate scenario analysis the model provides results within minutes, even for very large landscapes (such as our 59,000 km² study area). As input, the user must specify the initial state of the landscape and provide quantitative assumptions concerning future industrial activities, natural disturbances, and rate of regeneration for each disturbance type. Given this information the model tracks and updates the state of the landscape in one-year time steps for as long as requested.

When only forest harvesting and regeneration are activated, the model is functionally equivalent to the non-spatial timber supply models used by forestry companies for long-term harvest planning (Forestry Corporation, 2002). The major

Table 5.1. Area of the Al-Pac FMA in a non-forest state in 2002 resulting from industrial disturbance.

Type of disturbance	Area (ha)
Seismic lines	41,082
Pipelines	22,258
Roads (minor)	20,000
Pasture grass	19,992
Well sites	15,516
Roads (major)	11,606
Roads (well site)	7,346
Oilsand surface mine	5,829
Recreation areas	3,100
In-block losses	2,800
Towns	2,460
Misc. agriculture	1,809
Coal	1,947
Transmission lines	1,000
Peat mine	234
Miscellaneous	130
Total disturbed area	155,162

advance of *ALCES* is that the user can include a variety of additional natural and human-origin disturbances in model runs. The suite of available ecological output measures is also far greater than what is typically included in timber supply models.

In operation, the model continuously tracks the quantity of various landscape features (e.g., roads, wells). However, because the model is designed to operate rapidly, it does not track the spatial location of these features. For example, the model knows how many seismic lines there are within the study area, but it does not know where they are. To address this spatial limitation, *ALCES* permits users to stratify the landscape into subunits that are tracked independently. For example, the forest land base can be stratified by stand type, and different harvest and regeneration strategies can be applied to each stratum.

For some types of industrial activity new disturbances may overlap existing features. For example, new seismic programs are sometimes conducted along existing seismic lines that have not yet regenerated. Such an activity does not increase the total industrial footprint (though it does affect the state of regeneration). Because *ALCES* is not fully spatial it cannot directly account for the overlap of individual features. Instead, the user must specify the average proportion of new disturbances that overlap existing features. Changing the proportion of overlap of features between model runs may be an important component of a scenario comparison.

Modelling Assumptions

The analysis presented here is intended to illustrate the future state of the forest under current management policies and conventional operating practices. The disturbance types were limited to

forest harvesting, petroleum exploration and development, road construction, and fire. The model was run for 100 years into the future.

Forest harvesting protocols were matched to conventional practices in use in Alberta, as described in Chapter 3. The basic approach was a two-pass clearcut system with a target harvest age of 70 years for hardwoods and 100 years for softwoods. Stands older than the target harvest age were cut first, while they remained on the landscape. Regeneration systems and stand growth and yield curves were also matched to current industry norms. In-block haul roads and landings (which experience delayed regeneration) were assumed to occupy 5% of each cutblock.

The future trajectory of petroleum industry activities was based on the assumption that drilling would continue at the current rate (Fig. 5.3)

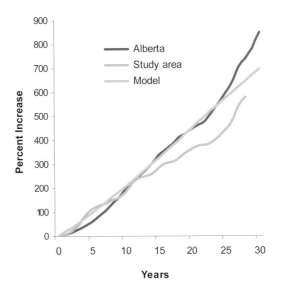

Fig. 5.3. Cumulative number of wells in the study area and Alberta, 1970-1999. Superimposed are the cumulative number of wells in the first 30 years of the model run. Data are expressed as the annual percent increase relative to year 0, to facilitate direct comparison.

until reserves are depleted (Fig. 5.4). Only 1% of the 315 billion barrels of potentially recoverable oil sands reserves have been recovered to date; therefore, oil sands reserves will last well into the next century (AEUB, 2001:2). Separate trajectories for conventional oil, gas, and oil sands were used in the model (Fig. 5.5).

Historical trend data on the rate of seismic line development were incomplete for the study area. However, from Al-Pac's GIS dataset we determined that an average of 3 km of seismic lines are generated for each well drilled and this relationship was used in the model runs. Similarly, we used a ratio of 0.1 km pipeline for each well drilled. Other petroleum sector variables are listed in Table 5.2.

Based on Al-Pac's road development plan, together with anticipated road construction associated with energy sector development, we estimated that 75 km/year of major roads would be

built over the next 50 years. At that point the major road network in the study area would be relatively complete. The construction of in-block haul roads and well site access roads was linked to the rate of harvesting and drilling, respectively.

Over the past two decades fire has burned an average of 0.65% of northern Alberta per year (excluding water bodies), and the rate appears to be trending upwards (see Chapter 6). Estimates of long-term rates of burn, based on mathematical analysis of forest age structure and fire history data, range from 0.4% per year (Cumming, 1997) to 2.2% per year (Murphy, 1985). Balancing these various sources of information we selected a burn rate of 1% per year for the model runs. Instead of varying the area burned from year to year we utilized a constant burn rate, so as to simplify comparison between alternative management scenarios. Fire salvage logging was not included in the model.

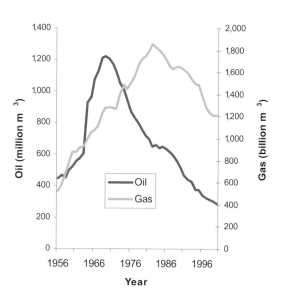

Fig. 5.4. Conventional oil and gas reserves in Alberta, 1956-2000. Source: AEUB, 2001 and earlier AEUB reports.

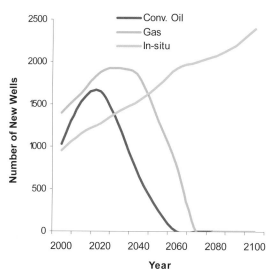

Fig. 5.5. Annual number of new wells used in the simulation, by product type.

Table 5.2. Description of current practices simulated in the model.

Variable	Simulated Practice
Harvest of hardwoods	Oldest first; minimum harvest age = 70 years.
Harvest of softwoods	Oldest first; minimum harvest age = 100 years.
Cutblock size	All cutblocks = 21-40 ha in size
In-block losses	5%
Road harmonization between the petroleum sector and forestry sector	10% sharing of new roads
Width of seismic lines	5 m
Reforestation of seismic lines	25 year lag (seeded to grass)
Spatial overlap of new seismic lines with existing linear disturbances	10%
Spatial overlap of new pipelines with existing linear disturbances	10%
Number of wells per drill pad	1
Reforestation of well sites after decommissioning	25 year lag (seeded to grass)

Model Results

Until about 1950, our study area could be characterized as boreal wilderness (Wetherell and Kmet, 2000). By 2000 it had undergone a profound transformation, as a consequence of accelerating industrial development (AEP, 1998b). However, this transformation pales in comparison to the changes we predict are yet to occur in coming decades unless changes are made to the current regulatory framework and operating practices.

According to our model there will be a progressive reduction in the forest land base, the remaining forest will become progressively younger and more fragmented, and there will be a marked increase in human access. The cumulative industrial footprint, in terms of landscape fragmentation by linear features and total area disturbed, will quadruple over the next 20-30 years, and then moderate (Fig. 5.6). The total length of

roads (after accounting for the reclamation of in-block haul roads) will rise from 17,764 km today to 162,000 km over the next 50 years (Fig. 5.6).

Because these predictions are for the most part based on a simple projection of current trends, they are relatively robust. Indeed, localized examples of development at the high intensities predicted by the model already exist in Alberta in areas where industry is mature (Fig. 5.7). Moreover, more than $50 billion dollars in new petroleum developments in northern Alberta have already been announced (ARD, 2001: 15). In cases where accurate estimates of model parameters were unavailable, conservative estimates were used so that the results would not be construed as a worst-case scenario.

The increase in fragmentation is primarily attributable to industrial features that persist on the

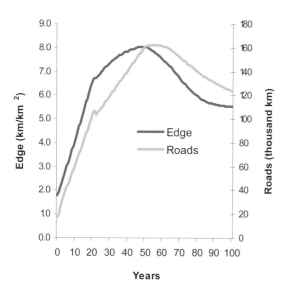

Fig. 5.6. Projected density of disturbance edge and length of roads in the Al-Pac FMA over the next 100 years.

landscape, leading to cumulative impacts far in excess of the annual rate of disturbance. Most prominent among these features are seismic lines, because they are generated at a high rate and require decades to regenerate under current practices (Revel, 1984; Osko and MacFarlane, 2001). Roads, well sites, pipelines, and in-block losses associated with harvesting are also important contributors to landscape fragmentation.

Given that conventional oil and gas reserves are already in a state of decline in Alberta (AEUB, 2001), the predicted rapid expansion in the industrial footprint over the next two decades is somewhat counterintuitive. However, the annual rate of production in the near term is primarily limited by economic factors and industry capacity, not the size of reserves. Provincial government policy is focussed on maximizing short-term eco-

1949

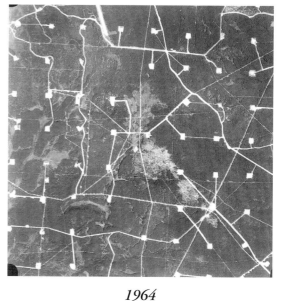

1964

Fig. 5.7a. Aerial photo time series illustrating cumulative industrial impacts in the Swan Hills (Twp. 63, Rge. 11, W5th). The dimensions of the figure are approximately 7 km by 7 km. The first photograph, taken in 1949, shows the area while still pristine. By 1964, oil wells (white squares) and access roads (white lines) had permeated the area. (Photos: Air Photo Services, Alberta Sustainable Resource Development)

70

1991

Fig. 5.7b. Aerial photograph of the same area as Fig. 5.7a (yellow square), and the surrounding landscape in 1991. By 1991 additional road development and petroleum activity had occurred, and the first pass of logging (large grey polygons) had taken place. The once thriving grizzly bear population in the Swan Hills had by this time been reduced to a few remnant animals. The scale is similar to the previous photographs, (Photo: Air Photo Services)

Alternative Futures

nomic returns from the remaining reserves, and the royalty system has been structured to ensure this occurs (Macnab et al., 1999). Petroleum companies share the desire to develop rapidly because there exists a risk that alternative forms of energy may reduce demand for petroleum in the future, and because oil that is extracted provides cash for investment, whereas oil in the ground does not. In consequence, the conventional oil and gas sector is poised to undergo a pronounced "boom and bust" cycle over the next 20-30 years, ending when reserves are depleted. The exception to this pattern is the development of oil sands deposits, which are sufficiently large to last well into the next century (AEUB, 2001).

Another structural change to the forest predicted by our model is the elimination of old-growth from the study area. Old-growth stands of softwoods (> 140 years) were lost within 20 years, and old-growth stands of hardwoods (> 100

years) within 65 years (Fig. 5.8). This result is the direct manifestation of current forestry practices in which oldest stands are logged first (AEP, 1994b: sec 2.2.1). Although forest clearing by the petroleum industry and fire do not target older stands specifically, they do remove some old growth by chance and hence increase the rate at which old-growth is lost.

Through our model runs, it also became evident that not even the timber supply was sustainable under the current system of management. A shortfall in timber will begin to be experienced by softwood operators in approximately 60 years (Fig. 5.9). In areas of the province where the forest industry is more mature this shortfall will occur even sooner and may also affect deciduous operators. Because mills have substantial fixed costs, running below full capacity translates into reduced economic return, and in some cases may result in mill closure. A further consequence is

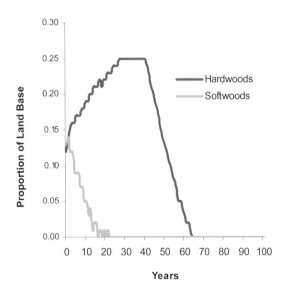

Fig. 5.8. Proportion of the study area in old-growth, projected over the next 100 years.

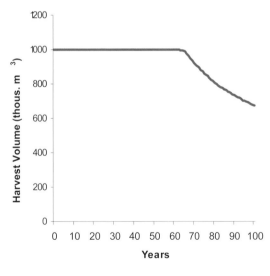

Fig. 5.9. Projected softwood harvest volume in the study area over the next 100 years.

that companies may abandon ecological management in favour of intensive forest management.

The timber shortfall occurs because annual harvest rates are currently set by the maximum rate of tree growth without accounting for losses from fire and the activities of the petroleum sector (AEP, 1996). Salvage logging cannot fully compensate for these external losses because more than half of the area of merchantable forest lost to fire and the petroleum sector is too young, too damaged, or too inaccessible to be used (Al-Pac, unpub. data). Moreover, as time passes and the forest becomes progressively younger, less and less wood lost to external causes is suitable for salvage and all sources of disturbance effectively become additive.

Field Studies

According to the *ALCES* model, the basic structure of the forest will undergo a dramatic transformation in coming decades. But how will this affect forest wildlife? To answer this question a variety of field studies have been undertaken in Alberta over the past few years.

The most compelling data, with respect to cumulative industrial impacts in an Alberta context, have been generated by the Adaptive Management Experiment Team, based at the University of Alberta (www.ameteam.ca). In 2001 this research group initiated a two-year study to examine the relationship between the abundance of selected wildlife species and total industrial footprint, at the township scale. In this study a series of townships that differed in the level of industrial use was selected within and around the Al-Pac FMA. Townships with little forest cover (e.g., containing large peat complexes) were excluded from the study. Within the selected townships field crews conducted systematic surveys of bird

populations (by listening for songs during the spring breeding season) and selected mammal populations (by conducting track counts during the winter). In total, 43 townships were sampled in the bird surveys and 70 townships were sampled in the mammal surveys.

Although the collection of data is still ongoing, and statistical analysis has not yet been completed, preliminary results from the initial year of study already demonstrate some clear trends. In the mammal survey, increasing industrial footprint was associated with a decline in the abundance of fishers (Boutin and Moses, unpub. data) (Fig. 5.10). Similar trends were evident in several of the resident and migratory bird species surveyed (Schmiegelow and Cumming, unpub. data) (Fig. 5.11). It is likely that even more marked declines in abundance would have been observed in the highly impacted sites had there not been a

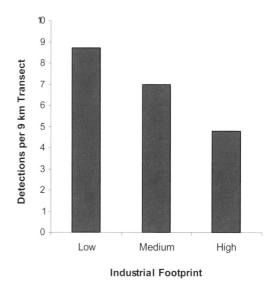

Fig. 5.10. Abundance of fishers in the Al-Pac FMA relative to the intensity of industrial footprint. Source: Boutin and Moses, unpub. data.

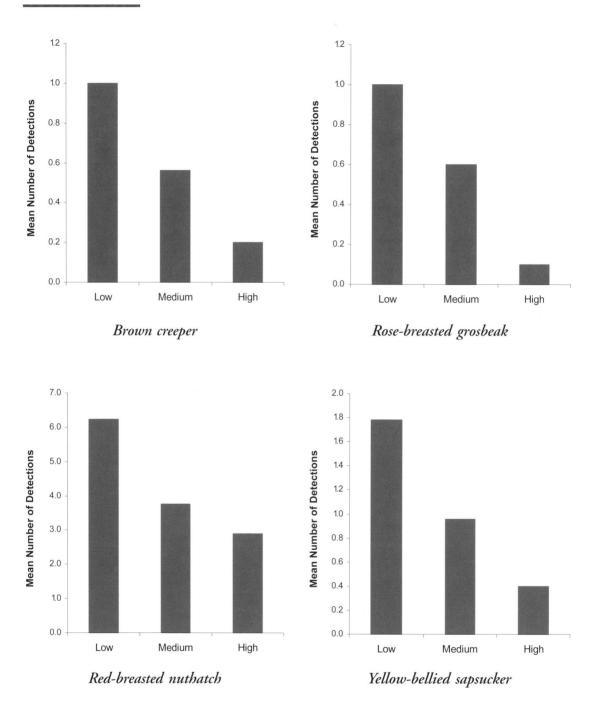

Fig. 5.11. Abundance of four species of birds in the Al-Pac FMA relative to the intensity of industrial footprint (low, medium, and high). Source: Schmiegelow and Cumming, unpub. data.

surrounding matrix of intact forest, providing a source of dispersing individuals (Donovan et al., 1995).

Seminal research on the ecological effects of industrial activity in Alberta's boreal forest has also been conducted by the Boreal Caribou Research Program (www.deer.rr.ualberta.ca/caribou/bcrp.htm). More than ten years of data from radio-collared caribou from across northern Alberta have now been collected through this program. These data were recently summarized in a provincial status report on woodland caribou (Dzus, 2001: 14, 30), which concluded:

> *The current distribution, intensity, amount, and type of human activity on and near caribou range is compromising the integrity of caribou habitat. Analyses for six study areas in northern Alberta suggest that caribou populations in most boreal ranges are declining.*

There appear to be several causes for the observed decline in caribou populations. Forest harvesting in or near caribou range results in abundant growth of new vegetation that tends to stimulate moose populations. Increased abundance of moose can in turn increase the presence of wolves, leading to higher mortality of caribou (James, 1999). Increased mortality of caribou may also occur through poaching and native hunting, as a consequence of increased access via roads and seismic lines (Dzus, 2001: 23). Finally, studies of radio-collared caribou have shown that caribou avoid industrial features, implying an effective loss of habitat that is much greater than the local area of disturbance (Dyer et al., 2001). The distance of avoidance ranges from 250 m for seismic lines to 1000 m for well sites. Additional studies have determined that the density of lin-

ear features in northern Alberta is already so high that 48% of the core caribou ranges are (on average) within the avoidance zone (Dzus, 2001: 25). Simulations using the *ALCES* model predict that habitat availability will continue to decline in the future (Fig. 5.12). Consequently, unless fundamental changes are made to the way industrial activities are managed, the extinction of woodland caribou from Alberta appears inevitable.

As a final note, the fact that extinctions have not yet been observed in Alberta's boreal forest is no cause for complacency. Extensive industrialization of northern Alberta is too recent a phenomenon for extinctions to have occurred. But one need only look to Europe, where industrial forestry has been practiced for an extended period, to gain insight into the long-term consequences of conventional industrial forestry. In Europe, declines and extinctions of bird and in-

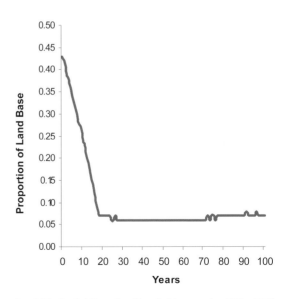

Fig. 5.12. Availability of caribou habitat on the Al-Pac FMA over the next 100 years, predicted by *ALCES* simulations.

sect species have both been documented and correlated to the intensity of industrialization (Siitonen and Martikainen, 1994; Angelstam et al., 1997; Mikusinski and Angelstam, 1998; Niemela, 1999). It has also been demonstrated that because of the progressive loss of old-growth forest, birds that require old-growth habitat are being concentrated in protected areas (Virkkala et al., 1994).

Summary of Part I

The Alberta Forest Conservation Strategy (AFCS) serves as an unassailable guide to the vision and goals held by Albertans regarding public forests. In spite of the fact that the government, forest industry, and petroleum industry were all signatories to the AFCS, the evidence I have presented here and in previous chapters suggests that the current system of forest management in Alberta is fundamentally inconsistent with the *Strategy*. The specific deficiencies of the current system are summarized below, using the Principles of the AFCS (AFCSSC, 1997: 4) as a framework.

Principle 1. Ecological Sustainability: *The forests of Alberta will be appreciated as ecosystems and our activities managed in ways that conserve ecological integrity, biological diversity, long-term forest productivity and the forest landbase.*

Deficiencies:
1. The rate of harvest by the forestry sector is too high. Annual allowable cut levels continue to be based on maximizing the flow of timber, not the capacity of the forest to absorb disturbance. Furthermore, the growth curves used in the calculations appear to be overly optimistic, and the addi-

tive effects of fire and clearing by the petroleum industry are not accounted for.
2. Harvest planning by the forestry sector does not incorporate meaningful ecological objectives (though two or three companies have made a start). Consequently, the basic structure of the forest is being transformed. Most significantly, old-growth stands are being eliminated from the landscape, as are mixedwood stands. The size of forest stands is declining and becoming more uniform, and natural patterns in the spatial distribution of patches are being altered.
3. Harvest practices by the forestry sector are still largely based on a simple multi-pass clearcut system (though a few companies are beginning to implement modifications). Clearcuts leave little structural legacy in the regenerating forest, which is detrimental to species adapted to natural disturbances that do provide such a legacy.
4. Regeneration of softwood stands continues to be based on plantation techniques, including invasive soil preparation, planting of genetically selected stock, and the use of herbicides to control competing vegetation. This form of regeneration presents another form of structural simplification of the forest, with negative implications for the conservation of biodiversity.
5. Effective controls on the landscape-level impacts of the petroleum sector are lacking. In contrast to the forestry sector, there are no annual limits on the rate of forest clearing by the petroleum sector, no cap on the cumulative intensity of activity in any given area, and no requirement for reforestation. The result has been and continues to be a

cumulative loss of forest and a dramatic increase in fragmentation and human access — all of which threaten the integrity of the forest and the associated biota.

6. The operating practices of the petroleum sector also have detrimental effects at the local level. Oil sands developments, including both mines and in-situ projects, have the greatest impact. In addition to the direct loss of forest, the most notable concerns include pollution of the soil, water, and air, erosion of soil, damage to aquatic systems, direct disturbance of wildlife, and reduction in supplies of fresh water.

7. Road construction continues at a rapid pace throughout the north, and there is no limit on the maximum road density in any given area. Roads are associated with a wide variety of negative ecological effects, including direct and indirect loss of habitat, fragmentation of habitat, disruption of water and fish movements, erosion of soil, changes in animal movement patterns, and increased access by humans (resulting in increased hunting, poaching, and roadkills).

8. A workable framework for integrated resource management is still lacking in the province. Under the current system, tenure rights are provided to multiple operators on the same land base and the management of these operators involves multiple governmental agencies with differing policy mandates. Because of the lack of an integrated planning framework, resource companies generally conduct their planning and operations independently. This situation makes it all but impossible to achieve landscape-level objectives and instead results in ecological impacts that are largely additive.

9. There has been no acceptance on the part of the government or industry that the forest has finite ability to meet the demands being placed on it. Forestry allocations and petroleum developments continue to be approved in the absence of defined limits on cumulative industrial impacts.

10. Minimal resources are being directed toward maintaining the viability of rare and endangered species. The few recovery plans in existence are largely comprised of measures that mitigate the most egregious industrial practices but do not go far enough to ensure the long-term viability of affected populations.

11. The evidence suggests that the political will to implement the AFCS is lacking, de-spite various policy statements affirming the government's commitment to sustainable forestry. The government's failure to define and champion meaningful and measurable ecological objectives means that management decisions at all levels continue to promote resource extraction over ecological concerns.

Principle 2. Economic Sustainability: *Human activities on forested lands in Alberta will be managed in ways that will provide sustained and enhanced, economic and other benefits for Albertans well into the future.*

Deficiencies:

1. Current rates of harvest are not sustainable. Because losses to fire and the petroleum sector are not accounted for, and because

growth assumptions are overly optimistic, there will be a decline in the timber supply in coming decades. This implies a loss of employment in the forestry sector (in addition to on-going losses from technological advancement).

2. As old-growth stands are liquidated the size of trees on the landscape will become progressively smaller. This will negatively affect mills that require large trees to produce dimensional lumber.

3. Current forestry practices are incompatible with the requirements of new forest certifications schemes (e.g., FSC, 2002). This means that forestry companies in Alberta may face restricted access to markets in the future if the current practices are maintained.

4. Petroleum royalties per barrel of oil equivalent are low in Alberta relative to other jurisdictions. This implies that Albertans are not receiving their full share of economic benefits from this resource. Furthermore, the unprecedented rate of development brought on by the low royalties is causing a great deal of environmental damage.

5. In addition to the ecological costs associated with the activities of the petroleum sector, there are also substantial unnecessary financial costs. These costs include timber damage fees paid to forestry companies, excessive road construction costs due to lack of coordinated planning, and foregone carbon credits.

Principle 3. Precautionary Principle: *Caution will be exercised when the consequences of actions in the forest are uncertain. Where there is a threat of serious or irreversible damage to any forest ecosystem, lack of full scientific certainty will not be used as a reason for failing to implement appropriate ecological measures to avert the threatened damage.*

Deficiencies:

1. The precautionary principle has yet to be incorporated into the decision-making process. First, no systematic effort been made to identify threats and uncertainties or to develop appropriate responses to such threats. Second, despite the deficiencies listed under Principle 1 there has been no substantive change in the basic approach to forest management in Alberta and no reduction in the rate of industrial development.

2. The system of protected areas in Alberta, vital to the management of risk from industrial development, remains incomplete. The existing system lacks adequate representation of all ecoregions (and representation of merchantable forest in general), individual sites are generally too small to maintain ecological processes and integrity, the total area of protection is insufficient, and buffers and connectivity corridors are lacking.

Principle 4. Adaptive Management: *Forest managers will employ the adaptive management approach in managing the forests of Alberta. This approach will be based on the best-available scientific information, ongoing research, and routine monitoring of all activities carried out in the forest to continuously improve our management techniques as we learn from experience and adapt to evolving conditions and demands.*

Deficiencies:

1. Although the term adaptive management is now commonly used, it would be difficult to find examples of the formal implementation of this approach in Alberta.
2. Key obstacles to the implementation of adaptive management are the absence of a comprehensive system for monitoring forest structure and biodiversity (though a provincial biomonitoring system is now being developed) and the lack of capacity for threat assessment and prediction.
3. The availability of ecological benchmark areas, providing a "control" or reference for industrial "experiments", is inadequate because the system of protected areas is incomplete.

Principle 5. Accountability: *Individuals, companies and governments, as forest users and as consumers of forest products, have a duty to minimize the adverse effects of their actions upon the forest. They will be accountable and responsible for all of their actions and decisions which affect the forest.*

Deficiencies:

1. The *Forests Act* is devoid of direct reference to forest management, except for a simple directive regarding sustained-yield. As a consequence, forest management in Alberta is governed almost exclusively through policy, not law. This means that major forest management decisions are neither subject to legislative scrutiny nor open to legal recourse. Moreover, the government cannot be held legally accountable for its failure to implement its own policies pertaining to forest sustainability.

2. Collectively, resource companies are profoundly transforming the structure of the forest and threatening its integrity, yet there exists no effective mechanism for holding companies accountable for their cumulative impacts on the forest.

Principle 6. Decision-making: *All Albertans will have the opportunity to contribute in meaningful ways to decisions that are important to them. Decisions affecting the forest will consider the entire spectrum of interests in a fair and open manner.*

Deficiencies:

1. Through consultative processes such as the AFCS, it has been firmly established that the public demands a balance between resource extraction and forest conservation. However, operational decision-making by the government continues to be focussed on maximizing short-term economic gains through resource extraction. This indicates that meaningful public input has yet to become a reality in Alberta.
2. Consultative processes are becoming increasingly regionalized. This effectively increases the voice of local economic interests while reducing or excluding the voice of urban Albertans (that generally place a priority on forest conservation). Furthermore, there are no independent organizations with the mandate and resources to provide scientific and technical support to these consultative processes.
3. Forest allocations continue to be made through closed-door negotiations involving government and industry (e.g., the recent Grande Alberta Paper negotiations). Not

only is the public excluded from these negotiations, but information on the negotiations can only be obtained through appeals to the Freedom of Information Process.

4. In contrast to many other jurisdictions, Alberta continues to be a very difficult place for the public to obtain baseline data on the forest and information on industrial activities.

Literature Cited

AEUB (Alberta Energy and Utilities Board). 2001. Alberta's reserves 2000 and supply/demand outlook 2001-2010. Statistical series 2001-98. Alberta Energy and Utilities Board, Calgary, AB. (Available at: www.eub.gov.ab.ca)

AE (Alberta Environment). 2000. Annual report on the implementation of Alberta's commitment to sustainable resource and environmental management: 1999-2000. Alberta Environment, Edmonton, AB. (Available at: www3.gov.ab.ca/env/irm.html)

AEP (Alberta Environmental Protection). 1994a. Natural regions of Alberta. Alberta Environmental Protection, Edmonton, AB.

AEP (Alberta Environmental Protection). 1994b. Alberta timber harvest planning and ground rules. Alberta Environmental Protection, Edmonton, AB. (Available at: www.gov.ab.ca/env/forests.html)

AEP (Alberta Environmental Protection). 1996. The status of Alberta's timber supply. Alberta Environmental Protection, Edmonton, AB. (Available at: www.gov.ab.ca/env/forests.html)

AEP (Alberta Environmental Protection). 1998a. The Alberta forest legacy. Alberta Environmental Protection, Edmonton, AB. (Available at: www.gov.ab.ca/env/forests.html)

AEP (Alberta Environmental Protection). 1998b. The Boreal Forest Natural Region of Alberta. Alberta Environmental Protection, Edmonton, AB.

AFCSSC (Alberta Forest Conservation Strategy Steering Committee). 1997. Alberta forest conservation strategy. Alberta Environmental Protection, Edmonton, AB. (Available at: www.borealcentre.ca/reports/reports.html)

Angelstam, P.K., V. Anufriev, L. Balciauskas, and A. Blagovidov. 1997. Biodiversity and sustainable forestry in European forests: how East and West can learn from each other. Wildl. Soc. Bull. 25:38-48.

ARD (Alberta Resource Development). 2001. Annual report 2000/2001. Alberta Resource Development, Edmonton, AB. (Available at: www.energy.gov.ab.ca)

Cumming, S. G. 1997. Landscape dynamics of the boreal mixedwood forest. Ph.D. Dissertation. University of British Columbia, Vancouver, B.C.

Donovan, T., R. Lamberson, A. Kimber, F. Thompson, and J. Faaborg. 1995. Modeling the effects of habitat fragmentation on source and sink demography of neotropical migrant birds. Cons. Biol. 9:1396-1407.

Dyer, S. J., J. P. O'Neill, S. M. Wasel, and S. Boutin. 2001. Avoidance of industrial development by woodland caribou. J. Wildl. Manage. 65:531-542.

Dzus, E. 2001. Status of the woodland caribou (*Rangifer tarandus caribou*) in Alberta. Alberta Ministry of the Environment, Edmonton, AB. (Available at: www3.gov.ab.ca/srd/fw/riskspecies/speciesatrisk/index.html)

FSC (Forest Stewardship Council). 2002. Annual report 2001-02. Forest Stewardship Council of Canada, Toronto, ON. (Available at: www.fsccanada.org/policies/index.shtml)

The Forestry Corporation. 2002. ALCES Timber supply validation: comparison of *ALCES* and Woodstock/Stanley. Prepared for Alberta Environment and the Alberta Forest Products Association.

James, A. R. 1999. Effects of industrial development on the predator-prey relationship between wolves and caribou in northwestern Alberta. Ph.D. Thesis, University of Alberta, Edmonton, AB.

Kennett, S.A. 2002. Integrated resource management in Alberta: past, present and benchmarks for the future. Canadian Institute of Resources Law, Calgary, AB.

Macnab, B., J. Daniels, and G. Laxer. 1999. Giving away the Alberta advantage. are Albertans receiving maximum revenues from their oil and gas? Parkland Institute, Edmonton, AB.

Mikusinski, G. and P. Angelstam. 1998. Economic geography, forest distribution, and woodpecker diversity in central Europe. Cons. Biol. 12:200-208.

Murphy, P. 1985. Methods for evaluating the effects of forest fire management in Alberta. Ph.D. Thesis, U. of British Columbia, Vancouver, BC.

Niemela, J. 1999. Management in relation to disturbance in the boreal forest. For. Ecol. Manage. 115:127-134.

Osko, T. and A. MacFarlane. 2001. Natural reforestation on seismic lines and well sites in comparison to natural burns or logged sites. Alberta-Pacific Forest Industries, Boyle, Alberta.

Pope, D. 2001. Integrated landscape management on the Alpac FMA. In: Oil and gas planning on forested lands in Alberta: overview of CIF-RMS technical session, March 23, 2001. Canadian Institute of Forestry, Edmonton, AB.

Revel, R. D., T. D. Dougherty, and D. J. Downing. 1984. Forest growth and regeneration along seismic lines. University of Calgary Press, Calgary, AB.

Siitonen, J. and P. Martikainen. 1994. Occurrence of rare and threatened insects living on decaying *Populus tremula*: a comparison between Finnish and Russian Karelia. Scand. J. of Forest Res. 9:185-191.

Schneider, R.R., J.B. Stelfox, and S. Boutin. 2002. The management of cumulative impacts of land uses in the Western Canadian Sedimentary Basin: a case study. SFM Working Paper. Sustainable Forest Management Network, Edmonton, AB. (Available at: http://sfm-1.biology.ualberta.ca/english/home/index.htm)

Virkkala, R., A. Rajasarkka, R. A. Vaisanen, M. Vickholm, and E. Virolainen. 1994. The significance of protected areas for the land birds of southern Finland. Cons. Biol. 8:532-544.

Wetherell, D. and I. Kmet. 2000. Alberta's north: a history, 1890-1950. University of Alberta Press, Edmonton, AB.

Part II
New Ideas

6. The Natural Disturbance Model

Ecological Forest Management

The long list of deficiencies associated with the current system of forest management in Alberta indicates that the status quo is no longer tenable. The current system is the product of another era, now out of step with public values and advancing knowledge of forest ecology. Fortunately, Alberta's forest management problems are not unique. Researchers across North America and Europe have spent more than a decade addressing these problems and a substantial body of literature describing alternative approaches now exists. Collectively, these new approaches define a new paradigm of forest management, termed Ecological Forest Management (EFM) (sometimes referred to as Ecosystem Management).

The objectives of EFM are to maintain key ecosystem processes, to conserve native biodiversity, and to provide a stable and sustainable flow of economic benefits from the forest for current and future generations (AFCSSC, 1997: 7). EFM includes the following core elements:

1. **The Natural Disturbance Model (NDM).** The maintenance of biodiversity in the presence of industrial resource extraction cannot be accomplished through the individual management of species because there are too many species in-

volved and our understanding of their needs is inadequate. The NDM is an alternative approach, based on the assumption that biodiversity can be maintained in the presence of industrial use if industrial practices are made to approximate natural disturbances. In practice, the NDM entails the management of human disturbances to maintain ecological patterns and processes within their typical range.

2. **Protected areas.** Because of limitations with the NDM, and the inherent unpredictability of natural systems, a complete reliance on the NDM to maintain biodiversity would entail substantial risk. The limitations of the NDM do not invalidate its use, but imply that a complementary system of management, specifically designed to maintain biodiversity, must be implemented on a portion of the land base. A system of protected areas capable of maintaining ecological integrity is best suited to this role. Additional roles of protected areas, within the context of EFM, include ecological benchmarks against which the success or failure of the NDM can be assessed, conservation of wilderness, and sites for future research on natural ecological processes

3. **Monitoring.** EFM recognizes that all management scenarios are, in effect, experiments with substantial levels of uncertainty regarding the outcomes. Consequently, monitoring is an integral component of EFM, designed to evaluate whether the system overall is responding as predicted. Using feedback from monitoring, adjustments can be made to assumptions, models, and management practices in an effort to rectify any observed deviations. This process of feedback and adjustment has been termed adaptive management.

4. **Rare and threatened species.** Some species, because they are endangered or highly sensitive to industrial activities, will require extra attention to ensure their viability. Where the range of these species cannot be fully incorporated into protected areas, modifications of the NDM will be required, including specialized restrictions on industrial activities.

5. **Research.** Research is required to support the implementation of the NDM by providing a more complete understanding of ecological processes, including natural disturbance regimes, and determining how human disturbances (e.g., clear-cutting) differ from natural disturbances (e.g., fire). Research is also required as part of the adaptive management process, to determine the causes of any observed deviations from desired management outcomes.

6. **Decision-making.** EFM is not a static set of prescriptions, but a process that evolves in response to changing public values and new scientific information. Rates of forest harvesting and other decisions pertaining to land and resource use are made within the context of the desired future forest, not the growth rate of trees or mill capacity. Furthermore, decision-making is based on a common regional framework that integrates the activities of all users. Public involvement is a key component in identifying and weighing the social, economic, and ecological values to be sustained in the de-

sired future forest. All of the information used in planning and decision-making processes should be available to those who wish to be involved.

This chapter provides a detailed review of the NDM. Other elements of EFM are discussed in subsequent chapters. I begin with a review of fire and forest succession, which are the key ecological processes that the NDM seeks to emulate in the boreal mixedwood forest. I then examine the landscape structures and patterns that arise from these natural processes. In the final section I review the implementation of the NDM.

Ecological Processes

Distribution of Fire Size

The vast majority of fires are small. Fires up to 2.0 ha in size account for 74% of all fires recorded in the provincial fire database from 1961 to 2000 (ASRD, 2002). A pattern of decreasing frequency with increasing size is also evident in Class E fires (i.e., those over 200 ha in size; Fig. 6.1). Although large fires are rare they are responsible for the majority of the area burned. For example, 98% of the area burned in Alberta from 1961 to 2000 was due to only 5% of the fires. These large fires, some of which have exceeded 100,000 ha in size, play a dominant role in structuring landscape patterns at the largest scales.

Patterns in Fire Occurrence over Time

Large fires are generally associated with so-called "fire years" in which extreme climatic conditions, including extended periods of hot and dry weather, make the forest highly susceptible to burning (Bessie and Johnson, 1995). During fire years multiple extensive burns can occur. For ex-

ample, in 1981 six fires occurred, each exceeding 100,000 ha in size.

Based on the provincial database of Class E fires an average of 0.65% of the land area in northern Alberta has burned annually since 1980. However, because of the influence of fire years the rate of burning over time has varied tremendously (Fig. 6.2), making it difficult to accurately characterize the mean rate of burning (Armstrong, 1999). Furthermore, studies of charcoal and pollen in lake sediments have demonstrated that the mean rate of burning has fluctuated widely over the centuries, likely in response to long-term climatic changes (Bergeron et al., 1998).

Since the 1950s fire suppression efforts have steadily increased in terms of dollars spent and area controlled (Murphy, 1985). By 1971 a policy of total suppression across the entire province was

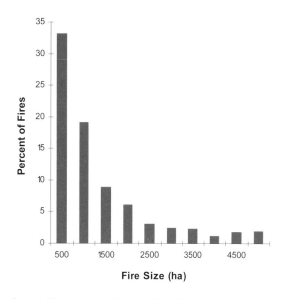

Fig. 6.1 Distribution of fire size for Class E fires in Alberta from 1961 to 2000. Only fires up to 5,000 ha are shown. Source: ASRD, 2002.

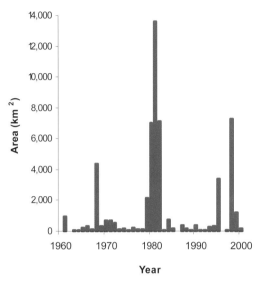

Fig. 6.2. Annual area burned in Alberta from 1961 to 2000. Source: ASRD, 2002.

in place (Murphy, 1985). Annual expenditures on fire suppression and control are currently $127 million (average for 1996-2000; CFS, 2002). But these efforts have not been accompanied by a decreasing trend in the annual area burned (Fig. 6.2). While there is some evidence that fire suppression has reduced the number and size of fires when climatic conditions are not extreme, suppression does not appear to have been effective in stopping large fire events (Larsen, 1997; Johnson et al., 1998; Campbell, 1999). Similar observations have been made elsewhere, indicating that Alberta is not unique in this regard (Agee, 1997; Moritz, 1997). It appears that large fires that occur during fire years, accounting for much of the area burned over time, are virtually unpreventable.

Spatial Patterns in Fire Occurrence

At the provincial scale the impact of large fires is clearly evident (Fig. 6.3). The patchy nature of

the burning causes substantial regional differences in the age structure of the forest. Many large regions in the province have not burned at all in the past 50 years. Although there is no clear pattern in the distribution of fires, differences in the rate of burning among Natural Subregions have been detected through statistical analysis (Andison, 1997).

At the landscape scale fire patterns are characterized by marked variability. After an extended period of hot and dry weather most types of forest are susceptible to burning and the patterns produced are primarily a function of wind speed and direction (Bessie and Johnson, 1995). Oblong fires oriented in the direction of the wind are typical (Fig. 6.4), though fires that burn for an extended period will have complex shapes due to changes in wind direction over time. The intensity of burning varies in response to weather variables (e.g., precipitation and wind speed), physical features of the landscape (e.g., slope), and stand type (Foster, 1983). Some patches of forest remain unburned because they were downwind of firebreaks such as lakes, streams, and wetlands (Eberhart and Woodard, 1987).

Under less extreme climatic conditions fires are often smaller and less intense and physical features of the landscape have a greater influence on their behaviour. For example, a fire break that produces an unburned island in an intense, rapidly moving fire might completely block the forward progress of a less intense fire (Eberhart and Woodard, 1987). Furthermore, when climatic conditions are not extreme forest stands will vary in their susceptibility to burning and thereby also influence fire behaviour (Bessie and Johnson, 1995). Recent studies have shown that the probability of a fire starting in aspen stands, and the proportion of available aspen that is burned in

Fig. 6.3. Distribution of Class E fires in northern Alberta from 1950 to 2000. (Map: ASRD, 2002)

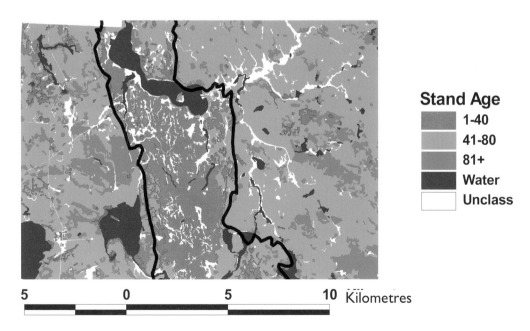

Stand Age
- 1-40
- 41-80
- 81+
- Water
- Unclass

5   0   5   10 Kilometres

Fig. 6.4. Stand age structure following a large fire that occurred in northeast Alberta in 1968. The fire (outlined in black) was 283 km^2 in size, of which 91 km^2 is shown. Note the arrangement of large patches of young forest produced by the fire and the patches of older forest within the fire boundary, representing fire skips. (Map: Forest Watch Alberta)

large fires, are both lower than in other forest types (Cumming et al., 1998; Cumming, 2001). This implies that the threshold for burning aspen stands is relatively high, though further research is required to confirm these findings.

Forest Succession

The following synthesis of forest succession in the boreal mixedwood was derived from papers by Kabzems et al., 1986: 62; Frelich and Reich, 1995; Cumming et al., 1996; Lieffers et al., 1996; Bergeron et al., 1998; Kneeshaw and Bergeron, 1998; Bridge and Johnson, 1999; Greene and Charron, 1999; and Cumming et al., 2000.

Although the intensity of burning within and among fires is variable, the large fires responsible for most burning generally kill most above-ground vegetation. The regeneration of the forest is influenced by a variety of regional and local site characteristics (e.g., moisture regime, soil type) and by availability of seeds. The result is that the large post-fire patches fairly rapidly differentiate into smaller forest stands that differ in vegetation composition and successional pathway.

Moisture regime has the greatest influence on forest succession. In the boreal mixedwood of Alberta moist sites are characterized by stands of black spruce and larch, medium sites by aspen and white spruce, and dry sites by pine. However, substantial variation exists within these coarse associations.

Succession on moist and dry sites is relatively straight-forward in that the original black spruce or pine stand is generally replaced with the same stand type after fire, though often with some component of aspen. Succession on medium sites is more complex. Aspen regenerates aggressively after fire through root suckering and is virtually always present in regenerating stands (even on sites previously dominated by white spruce, since few sites are completely devoid of aspen). The regeneration of white spruce is more variable. Regions within a burn that are more than about 100 m from the edge of the burn or from an unburned island will not be fully regenerated. Furthermore, seed production is variable from year to year and optimal production may not coincide with the immediate post-fire period which is best for seedling survival. Also, fire intensity influences the suitability of the seed bed. Hot fires that expose bare soil are required for optimal seedling germination and survival.

Because of the variability in white spruce regeneration, several outcomes are possible on medium sites. Wherever white spruce seed is available and the seedbed is suitable, an even-aged mixed stand of white spruce and aspen can be expected. Because aspen cannot regenerate in the shade of a conifer canopy the stand converts to pure spruce in approximately 100 years. If white spruce seed is available but the seedbed is unsuitable then the stand initially regenerates to aspen, but spruce enters incrementally (often germinating on old logs). The result is an uneven-age mixed stand, which also eventually becomes pure spruce, though over a longer period of time. Finally, if there is an inadequate source of white spruce seed, the stand regenerates to aspen, with or without scattered white spruce at low density. Instead of transforming to a white spruce stand the stand is more likely to become a self-perpetuating uneven-aged aspen stand. This occurs through incremental aspen regeneration in small forest gaps produced by wind damage or mortality associated with self-thinning. If the stand is not burned for a long interval (i.e., 200-300

years) the density of spruce may incrementally increase to the point of dominance.

The successional pathways for medium sites described above represent points along a continuum of possible trajectories. The relative frequency of occurrence of these trajectories at large spatial scales has not been determined, limiting our ability to interpret and predict landscape patterns.

Forest succession is influenced by other site characteristics in addition to moisture regime. Surface features and soil type are two of the most important factors, operating at both local and landscape scales. Because of unique combinations of moisture, soil, and surface features along riparian areas the composition of vegetation and age structure of stands here is usually distinct from the rest of the forest.

Forest Structure and Pattern

Stand Structure

Forest stands can be characterized by their structural attributes, including measures of the dominant tree species (e.g., density, percent canopy closure), understory, snags, and downed logs. These attributes undergo a predictable pattern of change as stands age and together they define a set of structural stages common to all stands types (Fig. 6.5). The duration of each structural stage differs among stand types because of differences in the rate of tree maturation. For example, aspen stands begin to acquire old-growth characteristics by 100 years, whereas stands of white spruce are still in the mature stage at this time (Timoney, 2001).

Much of the structure of young stands is due

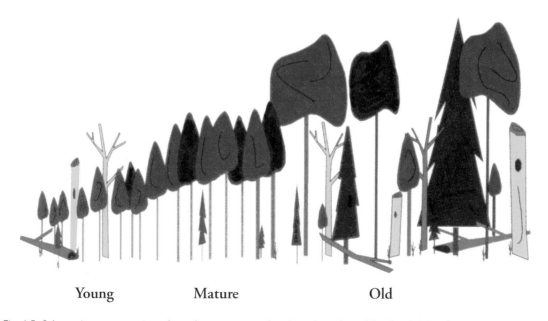

Young   Mature   Old

Fig. 6.5. Schematic representation of stand structure as a function of stand age (Graphic: I. Adams).

to the structural legacy left by the pre-fire stand. In all but the most intense fires, large trees are killed but not consumed and in time these dead trees become snags and then downed logs on the forest floor, providing structural diversity to the stand for several decades (Lee et al., 1997). Diversity in young stands is also enhanced by the openness of the canopy which permits light and warmth to reach the forest floor, stimulating understory growth. As a consequence of these multiple influences, structural diversity in young stands is intermediate between that of mature and old stands (Stelfox, 1995, *v*).

The transition of stands to the mature stage is marked by closure of the canopy. Mature stands are typified by a dense growth of relatively even-aged trees and reduced understory development (Stelfox, 1995: *v*). Self-thinning of the trees begins at this stage, but gap formation is not yet a prominent feature. The legacy of pre-fire aspen trees has diminished (Lee and Crites, 1999), though large-diameter conifer logs may persist. Mature stands have the lowest levels of structural diversity.

The transition from mature to old stands is gradual. The key changes include canopy breakup and release of understory plants, emergence of secondary canopy species, and accumulation of snags and downed logs (Stelfox, 1995: *v*). Relative to younger stages, old stands have trees of many ages and have more large canopy trees, large snags and large downed logs. Overall, structural diversity is highest in old stands and this is reflected in the highest species richness in both plants and animals (Stelfox, 1995: *vi*).

Stand structure is also influenced by stand type. The differences between coniferous and deciduous stands are of particular significance. Mixedwood stands, because they combine the features of both coniferous and deciduous stands, have a unique structural composition that is of importance to many species (Stelfox, 1995: *viii*).

Age Structure

If forests burned at a constant rate in a spatially random pattern then the age class distribution of stands would follow a curve similar to that shown in Fig. 6.6. The extended tail of this curve reflects the fact that through chance some stands escape burning for very long periods. The slope of the curve depends on the mean annual rate of burning. On actual landscapes this theoretical distribution is rarely observed, as illustrated by stands in Forest Management Unit L1 (2900 km^2; Fig. 6.6). The main reason for the discrepancy is that burning does not occur at a constant rate, but instead occurs in pulses associated with fire years (Fig. 6.2). Furthermore, most burning is clumped

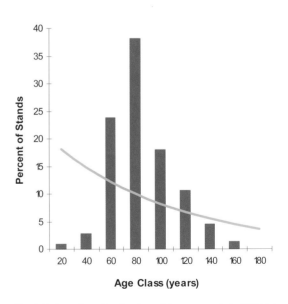

Fig. 6.6. Age class distribution of forest stands in FMU L1 (columns) and theoretical age distribution (line) assuming a constant rate of burn of 1.0% . Source: Al-Pac inventory.

as a consequence of large fires (Fig. 6.3). Because of these processes the age structure of the forest in any given area is more a function of the variability in fire occurrence, expressed locally, than it is of the mean rate of burning (Armstrong, 1999). This effect is most pronounced at small scales, but even at the provincial scale, equilibrium conditions are not observed due to long-term shifts in climatic conditions (Bergeron et al., 1998).

Stand Size

The distribution of stand size reflects an interplay between fire, site conditions, and forest succession. Large fires produce large uniform patches, albeit with many small unburned islands, and succession differentiates these patches into smaller units in response to differences in site characteristics and seed availability (Lieffers et al., 1996). The net result is that stand size is distributed in a pattern similar to forest fire size (Fig. 6.7), but on average, stands are substantially smaller than fires.

Stand size is quite sensitive to the system used to classify the landscape. An increase in the number of categories or resolution of interpretation results in a decrease in the average size of stands. In fact, highly detailed inventories, such as the Alberta Vegetation Inventory (AVI), virtually preclude the existence of stands greater than 100 ha (AEP, 1994). This issue must be considered when comparing landscapes and when developing size targets for NDM management.

Spatial Arrangement

The spatial arrangement of forest stands reflects the legacy of fire and local and regional differences in site conditions (Cumming et al., 1996). As a consequence of infrequent large fires, stands of the same age are typically aggregated together (Fig. 6.4). Within the matrix produced by these large fires lie patches of older forest, representing fire skips, and patches of newer forest arising from more recent small fires (Johnson et al., 1998).

Aggregation is also apparent from the perspective of vegetation type (Fig. 6.8). This is largely a consequence of regional patterns in site conditions, especially moisture regime (Bridge and Johnson, 1999). Although most of the boreal region is relatively flat, there are nevertheless significant differences in moisture regime expressed at a variety of scales up to multiple kilometres. These differences in moisture regime are in turn linked to different assemblages of vegetation (Cumming et al., 1996). Fire also plays a role in aggregating stands in that it promotes the establishment of aspen and mixedwood stands at the expense of pure conifer stands.

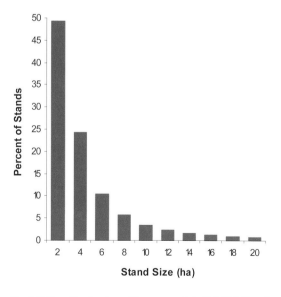

Fig. 6.7. Size distribution of forest stands in FMU L1. Stands > 20 ha are not shown. Source: Al-Pac inventory.

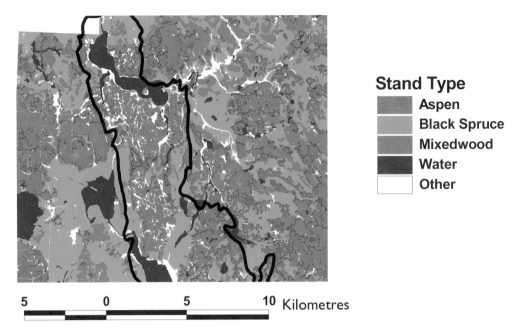

Fig. 6.8. Stand type for the same region illustrated in Fig. 6.4. Note the aggregation of similar stand types at a scale of multiple kilometres. Area labelled Mixedwood includes both mixedwood stands and pure white spruce stands.

The existence of large-scale aggregation notwithstanding, the spatial arrangement of stands at the local level is often highly complex (Fig. 6.9). This complexity reflects local variations in site conditions, seed availability, successional stage, and the irregular boundaries of past fires (Lieffers et al., 1996).

Aquatic features such as rivers, lakes, and wetlands also have an important influence on landscape patterns (Bergeron, 1991). Because they often act as fire breaks there is a greater probability of finding older forest stands in the vicinity of these features than in the remaining landscape (Timoney, 2001). Furthermore, the unique moisture regime, soils, and even microclimate in the vicinity of aquatic features lead to distinct assemblages of vegetation in these areas (Naiman et al., 1993).

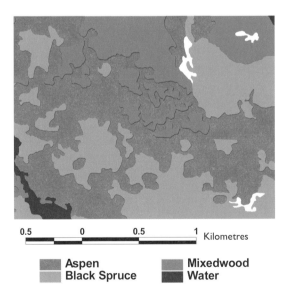

Fig. 6.9. Spatial arrangement of forest stands viewed at small scale. (Map: Forest Watch Alberta)

Relationship to Biodiversity

Forest species vary widely in their habitat requirements, reflecting diverse strategies for obtaining nutrition, avoiding predation, and meeting other requisites of life (Kirk et al., 1996). Many have specialized requirements reflecting physical and behavioural adaptations designed to minimize competition with other species. For example, the unique beak of the red crossbill, designed to efficiently pry open cones and extract the seeds therein, links this species to patches of coniferous forest with a high density of cones (Godfrey, 1986: 566). Because of such habitat specialization the overall diversity of forest species is dependent upon the diversity of habitat features, which is in turn a consequence of the combined actions of fire and succession (Bunnell, 1995; AFMSC, 1997: 3). Old-growth stands, because of their high structural diversity, generally have the highest levels of plant and animal species diversity (Stelfox, 1995: *vi*). In contrast, in Europe, where long-term traditional forestry has resulted in a simplification of forest structure and pattern, there has been a documented decline in species diversity (Siitonen and Martikainen, 1994; Mikusinski and Angelstam, 1998).

In addition to requirements for specialized habitat types, species also have requirements relating to patterns of habitat distribution. For some species stand size is of particular importance. For example, large stands are required for the optimal nesting success of some songbirds (Paton, 1994; Flather and Sauer, 1996). Another important aspect of habitat distribution is the spatial arrangement (interspersion) of stand types (Keitt et al., 1997). Frequently, a species will use one habitat type for cover and another for foraging, therefore both need to be in proximity (e.g.,

Romito et al., 1996). At large scales, the aggregation of similar habitat types noted previously may be important for the population viability of species that live in herds or those with limited ability for dispersal (e.g., Schaefer and Pruitt, 1991).

Landscape structure and pattern can also influence animal movement. Riparian zones are used as movement corridors by many species (e.g., Machtans et al., 1996). Also, the profound changes in landscape structure caused by disturbance events can reduce the general permeability of the landscape to animal movement (Donovan et al., 1995). In particular, many birds and mammals are reluctant to cross stands that have been intensely burned or clearcut because they lack sufficient cover (e.g., Steventon and Major, 1982; St. Clair et al., 1998).

It should be noted that natural disturbance and succession do not provide the habitat requirements for all species in all locations. The landscape is in constant flux, and the changes that occur, although temporary, often mean that species must move to survive (particularly after large disturbances). At any fixed location the abundance of many species will rise and fall (often suddenly) as the habitat features of the site change over time.

Forest Harvesting: The Natural Disturbance Model

Overview

Through natural selection the species inhabiting the boreal forest have developed adaptations for maintaining viability in the face of catastrophic disturbances such as fire (AFMSC, 1997: 3). In fact, periodic disturbance is necessary for the existence of species that depend on the earlier stages of forest succession. Based on these observations it has been suggested that biodiversity can be maintained in the presence of forest harvesting if harvest practices are made to approximate natural disturbances (Hunter, 1993). This forms the basis of the NDM approach to harvesting. Because fire is the dominant stand-replacing disturbance in the boreal mixedwood it has received the greatest attention within the context of the NDM in Alberta. Other disturbances such as insect damage and wind throw have been considered only superficially.

In practice, it is not the actual process of fire that the NDM seeks to approximate, but the structure and pattern resulting from fire and subsequent forest succession (Bergeron et al., 1999). In part, this reflects a recognition that fire and harvesting are fundamentally different processes (Niemela, 1999). Cutting and removing trees is not the same as burning them and leaving them in place, and even more importantly, infrequent large fires account for most of the area burned, whereas sustainable mill operation requires a relatively constant flow of timber from year to year. The assumption (and hope) is that the key to maintaining biodiversity is not necessarily the strict emulation of fire but the maintenance of habitat diversity, however that may be achieved (Bergeron et al., 1999).

Our ability to replicate the structures and patterns produced by natural disturbance is dependent on how well these structures and patterns can be characterized. The first consideration is the selection of a reference landscape. Because landscape structure and pattern change over time and space, due to the impact of large fires and long-term fluctuations in climate, there is no single "correct" landscape or time period to use

(Johnson et al., 1998). However, for the simple practical reason that historical landscapes cannot be adequately characterized, using the current landscape for primary guidance is the only realistic option available. The reference landscape should be large (e.g., FMA or Natural Subregion) to avoid undue influence from large historic fires. Also, areas that have already been significantly impacted by industrial use should be excluded from the analysis, or at least be subject to appropriate corrections.

Once a reference landscape has been defined the next step in the implementation of the NDM is the development of operational targets for the forest attributes that characterize forest structure and pattern. The key attributes amenable to measurement include those discussed throughout this chapter: within-stand structure, the distribution of stand type, age, and size, and the spatial arrangement of stands. The attributes are characterized using distributions instead of average values because of the NDM emphasis on maintaining the natural range of variability. Although I have to this point been using forest stands as the primary unit of measure, in practice it is more appropriate to use forest patches. Patches are simply aggregates of stands with similar features. The idea is to limit the number of different patch types to a quantity that is ecologically meaningful and tractable to work with. For example, a 50-year old aspen stand adjacent to a 60-year old aspen stand would be considered a single patch of "mature" aspen.

Within-patch Structure

Given the importance of the structural legacy left by the pre-disturbance stand (Stelfox, 1995: *vii*), post-harvest targets should be defined for the quantity and distribution of residual live trees, quantity and distribution of standing dead trees, and the quantity and distribution of downed woody material. Targets relating to soil nutrient levels and the disturbance and compaction of the forest floor after harvest should also be defined as these attributes may be affected differently by fire and harvesting (Xu et al., 1999).

Because harvesting in Alberta generally involves the removal of most large trees from a site, but fire does not, it would be impossible to achieve structural targets based on the strict emulation of fire (under current rates of harvest) (Niemela, 1999). Consequently, there has been an effort to define targets based on experimental studies that seek to quantify the minimum levels of post-harvest structure required for the maintenance of biodiversity. Recent research by the Alberta Research Council recommends that up to 30% of merchantable trees should be retained in within-stand residuals (Fig. 6.10), unharvested stands, and riparian buffers (Schieck and Song, 2002). Additional research will be required to determine how residual trees within cutblocks should be distributed for maximum benefit (e.g., size of clumps, spatial layout).

Given that fire has minimal influence on the structure of mature and old stands (Lee and Crites, 1999), the aforementioned targets for stand structure relate primarily to young stands. The unique characteristics of old-growth stands, particularly large live trees, large snags, and large downed logs, and the unique assemblages of plants and animals that are associated with them (Stelfox, 1995: *vii*), cannot be created through harvesting. Consequently, old-growth structure must be maintained by retaining older-aged stands on the landscape (Burton et al., 1999; Niemela, 1999).

Distribution of Patch Type

I use patch type to denote a specific combination of age and dominant tree species (e.g., old-growth aspen). The best available guide for the characterization of the target distribution of patch types is the current forest inventory. However, the extreme variability in annual area burned, reflecting the impact of fire years, distorts the distribution of patch age classes relative to the long-term mean, even at the scale of the largest FMAs (Cumming et al., 1996). Furthermore, forest inventories underestimate the proportion of older forest patches on the landscape (Cumming et al., 2000). Unfortunately, there are few options available for improving the estimated target distribution other than expanding the reference landscape to the maximum possible size (e.g., Natural Subregion) and removing biases in the inventory. Modelling techniques can offer qualitative guid-

Fig. 6.10. Recent cutblock demonstrating residual patches of trees left after harvest (Photo: Al-Pac).

ance, but because of deficiencies in our understanding of successional processes and rate of burning among patch types it is not currently possible to generate target patch distributions on the basis of theory.

A comparison between hypothetical targets for the NDM and sustained-yield management illustrates the major differences between these two approaches (Figs. 6.11 and 6.12). Whereas the NDM seeks to maintain the long-term mean distribution of patch types, sustained-yield management seeks only to maintain a continuous supply of timber. Consequently, under sustained-yield management older patch types and mixedwood patch types (and the habitat diversity they represent) are slated for elimination from the landscape (Bergeron et al., 1999).

The rate of harvest and the selection of harvest blocks both influence the distribution of

patch types through their effect on forest age structure (Bergeron et al., 1999). Harvest rates that exceed the rate of regeneration of old stands, or the preferential selection of older stands, will result in the loss of older age-class patches from the landscape.

The maintenance of targeted distributions over a typical 200-year planning horizon will require an iterative harvest planning approach involving computer modelling techniques. It should be noted that the distribution targets for patches are only intended to be met at the large spatial scales at which they were defined. At smaller scales (e.g., landscape) substantial variation can be expected, and should in fact be maintained; however, deviations should not exceed the range that is typical for a given scale.

The retention of mixedwood patches on the landscape requires changes to land management

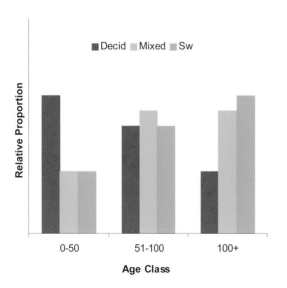

Fig. 6.11. Hypothetical NDM target distribution for patch types that are likely to be influenced by harvesting (Sw = white spruce).

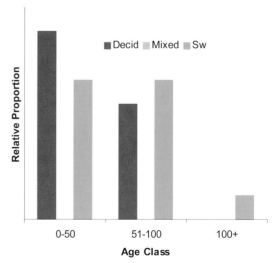

Fig. 6.12. Target distribution for patch types assuming sustained-yield management with an 80-year rotation for deciduous and 120-year rotation for conifer.

policies and practices. Currently in Alberta mixedwood stands are designated as either coniferous or deciduous, based on the volume of conifers at the time of inventory, and managed separately (generally by different operators) (Lieffers and Beck, 1994). Because of this separation of land bases, immature understory trees are generally not retained at harvest and regeneration efforts are (by regulation) intended to produce relatively pure stands, either through plantation techniques on coniferous sites or natural regeneration on deciduous sites.

In order to maintain mixedwood patches the dual land base system must be abandoned and mixedwood management techniques need to be employed (AFMSC, 1997: 4). Mixedwood management involves the promotion of a more natural process of regeneration in place of plantation techniques. So, for example, in harvesting a mature deciduous stand care would be taken to protect any existing coniferous understory. In time these retained coniferous trees would be available for harvest in a second entry to the site. Additional mixedwood techniques are reviewed by Lieffers et al. (1996). The abandonment of plantation management also lowers the likelihood of environmental disruption from techniques such as ground scarification, introduction of genetically selected trees, fertilization, and the use of herbicides (Lieffers and Beck, 1994; Easton and Martin, 1998). In addition to the ecological benefits, it has been suggested that the overall productivity of the land base is increased through mixedwood management and that increased overall economic returns can be anticipated (Lieffers et al., 1996). Mixedwood management may also be necessary for the viability of the sawlog industry as a shortage of large logs is anticipated un-

der the current short-rotation system (Lieffers and Beck, 1994).

Distribution of Patch Size

The distribution of patch size is much less variable than the distribution of stand age and can readily be derived from inventory data. Operationally, the easiest way of maintaining the size distribution of stands is to define harvest blocks on the basis of existing patch boundaries (see Fig. 6.9). However, for operational reasons it is difficult to fully emulate the natural distribution. Specifically, it is uneconomical to cut very small patches (e.g., < 2 ha) and there is public sentiment against the cutting of very large blocks (e.g., > 400 ha). The continued occurrence of small fires and the adoption of structured harvest techniques in place of conventional clearcutting will to some extent mitigate against the absence of very small harvest blocks. The maintenance of large patches can be achieved through careful planning of the spatial pattern of harvest.

Another issue that must be resolved is a tradeoff in the level of detail used to categorize patch types. If too many categories are used, large patches will be artificially fragmented and therefore be underrepresented in the target distribution. However, decreasing the number of habitat categories increases the likelihood that unique habitat types will be missed. Therefore, a balance must be sought.

The main difference between the NDM target for patch size and the sustained-yield management target is again variability (Fig. 6.13). The NDM seeks to maintain a natural range of patch sizes, whereas the targeted patch size under sustained-yield management is typically fixed for each stand type.

Spatial Arrangement of Patches

Although computer programs such as FragStats can quantify many aspects of landscape pattern, the full measure of complexity cannot be sufficiently characterized to establish a meaningful target. The alternative is to use the actual landscape as a guide.

In contrast to the NDM, the selection of harvest blocks under sustained-yield management is based on commercial value and accessibility. There are no landscape pattern objectives.

As illustrated in Figs. 6.4 and 6.8, the aggregation of similar patch types at large spatial scales is a prominent feature of forest landscapes. However, the maintenance of these large-scale patterns is one of the most difficult aspects of the NDM to implement. The problem is that large-scale patterns are in large part the result of intermittent fires that burn large areas irrespective of patch

type, whereas forest harvesting seeks to remove selected patch types at a constant rate from the entire management area. Furthermore, the extensive road network that is established to gain access to stands at the time of harvest results in continued disturbance by other forest users (Hunter, 1993). Little research has been conducted on this issue to date; however, it seems obvious that a shift away from dispersed harvesting will be necessary. Large patches of old-growth are likely at greatest risk; therefore, long-term regional planning that ensures the continual existence of such patches on the landscape (e.g., old-growth reserves) should be a priority (Niemela, 1999). Special attention must also be given to riparian zones and wetlands as these regions generally contain unique vegetation patterns that must be maintained (Naiman et al., 1993).

At the local scale, natural shape and local arrangement of patches can be maintained by defining harvest blocks on the basis of existing patch boundaries (see Fig. 6.9). In contrast to the NDM, sustained-yield management makes no attempt to maintain natural landscape patterns; harvest blocks are generally uniform in size and shape and are laid out in a simple grid pattern (Fig. 3.6).

Habitats Types not Maintained by the NDM

Although it should be possible to maintain the majority of habitat types using the NDM, certain habitat types may require special attention. For example, the dead trees remaining after fire constitute critical foraging habitat for black-backed woodpeckers as well as other species (Murphy and Lehnhausen, 1998; Schieck and Song, 2002). Habitat types such as these, that cannot be replicated through harvesting, must be maintained on

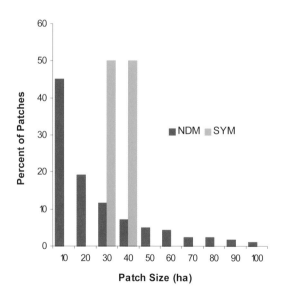

Fig. 6.13. Hypothetical target distribution of patch size for the NDM and sustained-yield management (SYM).

the landscape through alternative methods in sufficient amounts to ensure the viability of species that depend on them. In the case of post-burn stands this may mean that a proportion of naturally burned stands must be left unsalvaged (Schieck and Song, 2002). In addition to the maintenance of unique habitat types consideration must also be given to the habitat requirements of species that are rare or at risk of extinction.

Misuse of the NDM

Operating within the range of natural variability does not mean that a forestry company can transform the entire forest under its management to the conditions existing at some arbitrarily chosen place and time. If the NDM is properly applied, there should be no significant shifts in the current state of the forest at the regional scale. Variability, which is indeed an important component of the NDM, is primarily expressed at the local scale.

Literature Cited

Agee, J. 1997. Fire management for the 21st century. Pages 191-201 in Kohm, K., and J. Franklin, editors. Creating a forestry for the 21st century: the science of ecosystem management. Island Press, Washington, D.C.

AEP (Alberta Environmental Protection). 1994. Alberta vegetation inventory standards manual. Alberta Environmental Protection, Edmonton, AB.

AFCSSC (Alberta Forest Conservation Strategy Steering Committee). 1997. Alberta forest conservation strategy. Alberta Environmental Protection, Edmonton, AB. (Available at: www.borealcentre.ca/reports/reports.html)

AFMSC (Alberta Forest Management Science Council). 1997. Sustainable forest management and its major elements. Report prepared for Alberta Environmental Protection, Edmonton, AB. (Available at: www.borealcentre.ca/reports/reports.html)

ASRD (Alberta Sustainable Resource Development).

2002. Provincial wildfire database, on-line. (Available at: www3.gov.ab.ca/srd/)

Andison, D. 1997. Landscape fire behavior patterns in the Foothills Model Forest. Foothills Model Forest, Hinton, AB.

Armstrong, G. 1999. A stochastic characterization of the natural disturbance regime of Alberta's boreal forest: a simple process producing complex outcomes. Can. J. For. Res. 29:424-433.

Bergeron, Y. 1991. The influence of island and mainland lakeshore landscapes on boreal forest fire regimes. Ecology 72:1980-1992.

Bergeron, Y., P. Richard, C. Carcaillet, S. Gauthier, M. Flannigan, and Y. T. Prairie. 1998. Variability in fire frequency and forest composition in Canada's southeastern boreal forest: a challenge for sustainable forest management. Cons. Ecol., 2. (Available at: www. consecol.org/vol2/iss2/art6)

Bergeron, Y., B. Harvey, A. Leduc, and S. Gauthier. 1999. Forest management guidelines based on natural disturbance dynamics: stand and forest-level considerations. For. Chron. 75:49-54.

Bessie, W. C., and E. A. Johnson. 1995. The relative importance of fuels and weather on fire behavior in sub-alpine forests. Ecology 76:747-762.

Bridge, S., and E. Johnson. 1999. Geomorphic principles of terrain organization and vegetation gradients. Pages 446-455 in Proceedings of the 1999 Sustainable Forest Management Network Conference. Sustainable Forest Management Network, Edmonton, AB.

Bunnell, F. 1995. Forest-dwelling vertebrate faunas and natural fire regimes in British Columbia: patterns and implications for conservation. Cons. Biol. 9:636-644.

Burton, P., D. Kneeshaw, and D. Coates. 1999. Managing forest harvesting to maintain old growth in boreal and sub-boreal forests. For. Chron. 75:623-631.

Campbell, I. 1999. Palaeoecological reconstruction of holocene fire chronology and associated changes in forest composition in northern Alberta and Saskatchewan. Project Report 1999-7, Sustainable Forest Management Network, Edmonton, AB. (Available at: http://sfm-1.biology. ualberta.ca/english/home/index.htm)

CFS (Canadian Forest Service). 2002 National forestry database, on-line. Table 7.7: Protection expenditures on forest management by source of funding and province/territory, 1990-1999 (Available at: http://nfdp.ccfm.org/framesinv_e.htm)

Cumming, S. 2001. Forest type and wildfire in the Alberta boreal mixedwood: what do fires burn? Ecol. Appl. 11: 97-110.

Cumming, S., P. Burton, and B. Klinkenberg. 1996. Boreal mixedwood forests may have no "representative" regions: some implications for reserve design. Ecography 19:162-180.

Cumming, S., D. Demarchi, and C. Walters. 1998. A grid-based spatial model of forest dynamics applied to the boreal mixedwood region. Working Paper 1998-8, Sustainable Forest Management Network, Edmonton, AB. (Available at: http://sfm-1.biology. ualberta.ca/english/home/index.htm)

Cumming, S., F. Schmiegelow, and P. Burton. 2000. Gap dynamics in boreal mixedwood aspen stands: is the forest older than we think? Ecol. Appl. 10:744-759.

Donovan, T., F. Thompson, J. Faaborg, and J. Probst. 1995. Reproductive success of migratory birds in habitat sources and sinks. Cons. Biol. 9:1380-1395.

Easton, W. E., and K. Martin. 1998. The effect of vegetation management on breeding bird communities in British Columbia. Ecol. Appl. 8:1092-1103.

Eberhart, K., and P. Woodard. 1987. Distribution of residual vegetation associated with large fires in Alberta. Can. J. For. Res. 17:1207-1212.

Flather, C. H., and J. R. Sauer. 1996. Using landscape ecology to test hypotheses about large-scale abundance patterns in migratory birds. Ecology 77:28-35.

Foster, D. 1983. The history and pattern of fire in the boreal forest of southeastern Labrador. Can. J. Bot. 61:2459-2470.

Frelich, L. E., and P. B. Reich. 1995. Spatial patterns and succession in a Minnesota southern-boreal forest. Ecol. Monog. 65:325-346.

Godfrey, W. E. 1986. The birds of Canada. National Museum of Canada, Ottawa, ON.

Greene, D. and I. Charron. 1999. Simple models of asexual and sexual tree recruitment into recent large disturbances. Pages 116-120 in Proceedings of the 1999 Sustainable Forest Management Network conference. Sustainable Forest Management Network, Edmonton, AB.

Hunter, M. L. 1993. Natural fire regimes as spatial models for managing boreal forests. Biol. Cons. 72:115-120.

Johnson, E. A., K. Miyanishi, and J. M. H. Weir. 1998. Wildfires in the western Canadian boreal forest: landscape patterns and ecosystem management. J. Veg. Sci. 9:603-610.

Kabzems, A., A. Kosowan, and W. Harris. 1986. Mixed-wood section in an ecological perspective: Saskatchewan. Saskatchewan Parks and Renewable Resources, Regina, SK.

Keitt, T., Urban, D., and B. Milne. 1997. Detecting critical scales in fragmented landscapes. Cons. Ecol., 1. (Available at: www.consecol.org/vol1/iss1/art4)

Kirk, D., A. Diamond, K. Hobson, and A. Smith. 1996. Breeding bird communities of the western and northern Canadian boreal forest: relationship to forest type. Can. J. of Zool. 74:1749-1770.

Kneeshaw, D., and Y. Bergeron. 1998. Canopy gap characteristics and tree replacement in the southeastern Boreal Forest. Ecology 79:783-794.

Larsen, C. 1997. Spatial and temporal variations in boreal fire frequency in northern Alberta. J. Biogeog. 24:663-673.

Lee, P., and S. Crites. 1999. Early successional deadwood dynamics in wildfire and harvest stands. Pages 65-85 in Lee, P., editor. Fire and harvest residual project: the impact of wildfire and harvest residuals on forest structure and biodiversity in aspen-dominated boreal forests of Alberta. Alberta Research Council, Vegreville, AB.

Lee, P. C., S. Crites, M. Nietfeld, H. V. Nguyen, and J. B. Stelfox. 1997. Characteristics and origins of deadwood material in aspen-dominated boreal forests. Ecol. Appl. 7:691-701.

Lieffers, V., and J. Beck. 1994. A semi-natural approach to mixedwood management in the prairie provinces. For. Chron. 70:260-264.

Lieffers, V., R. Macmillan, D. MacPherson, K. Branter, and J. Stewart. 1996. Semi-natural and intensive silvicultural systems for the boreal mixedwood forest. For. Chron. 72:286-292.

Machtans, C., M. Villard, and S. Hannon. 1996. Use of riparian buffer strips as movement corridors by forest birds. Cons. Biol. 10:1366-1379

Mikusinski, G., and P. Angelstam. 1998. Economic geography, forest distribution, and woodpecker diversity in central Europe. Cons. Biol.12:200-208.

Moritz, M. A. 1997. Analyzing extreme disturbance events: fire in Los Padres National Forest. Ecol. Appl. 7:1252-1262.

Murphy, E. C., and W. A. Lehnhausen. 1998. Density and foraging ecology of woodpeckers following a stand-replacement fire. J.Wildl. Manage. 62:1359-1372.

Murphy, P. 1985. The effects of forest fire management in Alberta. Ph.D. Thesis, U. of British Columbia, Vancouver, BC.

Naiman, R., H. Decamps, and M. Pollock. 1993. The role of riparian corridors in maintaining regional bio-diversity. Ecol. Appl. 3:209-212.

Niemela, J. 1999. Management in relation to disturbance in the boreal forest. For. Ecol. Manage. 115:127-134.

Paton, P. 1994. The effect of edge on avian nest success: how strong is the evidence? Cons. Biol. 8:17-26.

Romito, T., K. Smith, B. Beck, and J. Beck. 1996. Moose (*Alces alces*) draft habitat suitability index model. Pages 151-157 in Beck, B., J. Beck, J. Bessie, and R. Bonar, editors. Habitat suitability index models for 35 wildlife species in the Foothills Model Forest. Foothills Model Forest, Hinton, AB.

Schaefer, J. A., and W. O. Pruitt. 1991. Fire and woodland caribou in southeastern Manitoba. Wildl. Monog. 116:1-39.

Schieck, J. and S. J. Song. 2002. Responses of boreal birds to wildfire and harvesting. Pages 9-1 to 9-45 in Song, S. J., editor. Ecological basis for stand management: a synthesis of ecological responses to wildfire and harvesting. Alberta Research Council, Vegreville, AB.

Siitonen, J., and P. Martikainen. 1994. Occurrence of rare and threatened insects living on decaying *Populus tremula*: a comparison between Finnish and Russian Karelia. Scand. J. of Forest Res. 9:185-191.

St. Clair, C. C., M. Bélisle, A. Desrochers, and S. Hannon. 1998. Winter responses of forest birds to habitat corridors and gaps . Cons. Ecol., 2. (Available at: www.consecol.org/vol2/iss2/art13)

Stelfox, J. B. 1995. Relationships between stand age, stand structure, and biodiversity in aspen mixedwood forests in Alberta. Alberta Environmental Centre, Vegreville, AB. (Available at: www.borealcentre.ca/reports/reports. html)

Steventon, J. D., and J. T. Major. 1982. Marten use of habitat in a commercially clear-cut forest. J. Wildl. Manage. 46:175-182.

Timoney, K. 2001. Types and attributes of old-growth forests in Alberta, Canada. Nat. Areas J. 21: 282-300.

Xu, J., P. Yeung, and P. Lee. 1999. Comparison of soil nutrients between wildfire and harvest stands. Pages 30-55 in Lee, P., editor. Fire and Harvest Residual Project: The Impact of Wildfire and Harvest Residuals on Forest Structure and Biodiversity in Aspen-Dominated Boreal Forests of Alberta. Alberta Research Council. Vegreville, AB.

R. Schneider

7. Protected Areas

Limitations of the Natural Disturbance Model

The fundamental assumption of the Natural Disturbance Model (NDM) is that biodiversity can be maintained in the presence of industrial use of the forest if industrial practices are made to approximate natural disturbances (Hunter, 1993). In practice, the goal is to maintain forest structures and patterns similar to those produced by fire and succession. However, the NDM has a substantial number of inherent limitations that make the conservation of all species highly improbable under this model. These limitations do not invalidate the NDM, but imply that a complementary system of management, specifically designed to maintain biodiversity, must be implemented on a portion of the land base.

Problems in Defining the NDM Targets.

The first step in the implementation of the NDM is to define operational targets that provide a close approximation to the natural disturbance regime. However, because of the extreme variability in fire occurrence (see Fig. 6.2), and the limited availability of fire-history data, the mean rate of burning cannot be accurately determined for Alberta (Armstrong, 1999). Furthermore, Cumming (2001) has demonstrated that the rate of burning differs among stand types, implying that even if the mean rate of burning were known for the province, it would not be sufficient to predict landscape patterns. The characterization of other forms of natural disturbance is even less developed than for fire. Finally, there are major gaps in our understanding of forest succession, particularly for mixedwood stands which have multiple potential outcomes after disturbance (Lieffers and Beck, 1994).

An alternative approach is to base operational targets on the forest structures and patterns that result from fire, as reflected in forest inventory data and field studies. This approach also has several limitations. In particular, even at large scales (e.g., FMAs) inventory data are influenced by the legacy of large fires (Cumming et al., 1996). The variability introduced by these large but infrequent fires effectively obscures long-term trends. Forest inventories also systematically underestimate the age of older forest stands (Cumming et al., 2000), and the effects of fire suppression and pre-existing industrial use may further confound the determination of the natural patterns. Finally, given that the current inventory represents just a "snapshot" in time, the determination of the range of natural variation over time remains an unresolved issue.

As a consequence of the aforementioned problems, the targets we define for the implementation of the NDM are necessarily coarse and of unknown reliability. Furthermore, because the targets are based on a very limited number of attributes (i.e., those that are amenable to measurement), they provide only a partial characterization of forest structure and pattern. Ecological processes are for the most part represented only indirectly, and disturbances other than fire are generally ignored. The implication of these limitations is that natural patterns and processes cannot be truly emulated — a target that cannot be defined cannot be achieved. This represents a risk that the NDM will not be successful in realizing its goal of maintaining biodiversity.

Differences between the NDM and Fire

Our ability to emulate natural patterns and processes under the NDM is further limited by a number of fundamental differences between fire and industrial use of the forest. Foremost among these differences is the road infrastructure that by necessity accompanies industrial operations (Fig. 7.1). Roads result in habitat loss, reduced habitat effectiveness through fragmentation, altered permeability of the landscape to animal movement, negative impacts on aquatic systems, and increased human access (resulting in increased

Fig. 7.1. Forestry access road (Photo: Al-Pac)

hunting and poaching) (Reed et al., 1996; Trombulak and Frissell, 2000). Other linear disturbances, such as seismic lines, pipeline corridors, and power transmission lines add to the fragmentation and access problems resulting from roads (see Chapter 4). None of these linear disturbances has a natural analogue in fire or any other natural disturbance.

Another key difference between fire and forest harvesting is that most burning occurs in infrequent large fires associated with "fire years", whereas sustainable mill operation requires a relatively constant flow of timber from year to year (Armstrong et al., 1999). Furthermore, harvesting operations target only merchantable stands, whereas fire affects all forest types (Armstrong et al., 1999). Consequently, the landscape patterns produced by fire and harvesting are fundamentally different.

Several additional differences between fire and forestry operations are apparent at the stand scale. Forest harvesting, by definition, involves the removal of most trees from a harvest block, whereas fire generally kills trees but leaves them in place. Even when attempts are made during harvest to leave residual trees on the site, the amount of structure left is only a fraction of what generally remains after fire. Furthermore, residual live trees do not have the same ecological function as charred dead trees (e.g., Murphy and Lehnhausen, 1998). The removal of trees from a site can also result in cumulative nutrient depletion (Xu et al., 1999). Erosion, soil compaction, and site preparation (e.g., ploughing) are additional byproducts of forestry operations that differ from fire (Keenan and Kimmins, 1993). Finally, regeneration techniques, even under mixedwood management (Lieffers and Beck,

1994), remain focussed on speeding the regeneration of conifers over rates that would occur naturally.

Each of the aforementioned differences between fire and industrial use of the forest represents a violation of the fundamental assumption of the NDM. This constitutes further risk that the NDM will not be successful in realizing its goal of maintaining biodiversity.

Problems in Implementation

Additional difficulties in the emulation of natural processes and patterns relate to limitations in our ability to implement the planning and practices necessary to realize NDM targets. Economic constraints, in particular, play an important role in determining the extent to which companies can and will implement practices in support of the NDM. Several key elements of the NDM, such as the retention of merchantable old-growth stands and the retention of residual trees on cutblocks, decrease the volume of timber available for harvest (Armstrong et al., 1999). For companies with limited flexibility in wood supply (i.e., most coniferous-based operations) a reduction in annual allowable cut may translate into reduced economic return. As a consequence, few companies are likely to completely implement the NDM unless required to do so.

There are also a number of logistical and technical constraints that impede the implementation of the NDM. For example, the scheduling of stands for harvest must be planned far into the future so that uncommon stand types and age classes are not periodically lost from the landscape and so that natural spatial patterns are maintained. At large spatial scales such planning can only be done with computer models; however, the harvest planning models currently in use (e.g., GIS-FORMAN, Stanley, Woodstock) cannot incorporate ecological outcomes into the modelling process. Furthermore, these models also fail to incorporate the impacts of wildfire, and they utilize simplistic assumptions concerning forest regeneration and succession.

Given that the petroleum industry annually disturbs an area of forest similar to that of the forestry industry (see Chapter 4) it will be impossible to achieve NDM landscape targets unless petroleum industry activities are integrated into the NDM planning process. However, petroleum companies plan on very short time scales (months to years) and at small spatial scales (most leases are less than a township in size). Furthermore, there are currently no legislated requirements for maintaining natural landscape patterns and no limits on the cumulative impact of their activities (see Chapter 4). Consequently, getting the petroleum sector involved in long-term landscape-scale planning, with new limits on exploration and extraction activities, is likely to be problematic and presents a serious barrier to the successful implementation of the NDM.

Past and present government policy presents another barrier to the implementation of the NDM. Almost all of the merchantable forest has been allocated on the basis of sustained-yield management (AEP, 1996a: 17), and annual allowable cut rates and operating regulations continue to be based on this approach. Furthermore, losses of timber due to fire and the activities of the petroleum sector are still not being accounted for. As a consequence, there remains little flexibility in the existing system for reducing harvest levels under the NDM. A large-scale reallocation of the timber supply on a combined deciduous/coniferous land base could provide much of the re-

quired flexibility (Cumming and Armstrong, 1999), but there is no indication that the government is willing to implement such changes.

The above limitations in our ability to implement the NDM (among others that were not specifically mentioned) make it unlikely that NDM targets can be achieved, however they are defined. This constitutes additional risk that the NDM will not be successful in maintaining biodiversity.

Roles of Protected Areas

Maintenance of Biodiversity

Given the aforementioned limitations of the NDM, and the inherent unpredictability of natural systems, a complete reliance on the NDM to maintain biodiversity would entail substantial risk and would violate the Precautionary Principle, as described in the Alberta Forest Conservation Strategy (AFCSSC, 1997: 4):

> Caution will be exercised when the consequences of actions in the forest are uncertain. Where there is a threat of serious or irreversible damage to any forest ecosystem, lack of full scientific certainty will not be used as a reason for failing to implement appropriate ecological measures to avert the threatened damage.

The limitations of the NDM do not invalidate its use, but imply that a complementary system of management, specifically designed to maintain biodiversity, must be implemented on a portion of the land base (Noss, 1992). This is the primary role of protected areas (EC, 1995: 22). A system of protected areas designed and managed to maintain ecological integrity can provide a refuge for populations that are adversely affected by industrial activities and a source for repopulation of the industrial land base once del-eterious operations are identified and changed (Noss, 1992).

Ecological Benchmarks

Protected areas also serve as ecological bench-marks in support of adaptive management, an-other integral component of Ecological Forest Management (Walters and Holling, 1990; Gund-erson, 1999). Under adaptive management, op-erational plans are considered to be experiments, not fixed expectations. Central to this approach is an ongoing evaluation of whether the system is responding as predicted, and whether desired management outcomes are being achieved (AFMSC, 1997: 11). Using this feedback, adjust-ments can be made to assumptions, models, and operating practices in an effort to rectify any ob-served deviations.

As with any experimental approach, adaptive management requires reference areas (controls) to provide a contrast to the experimental treatments (i.e., industrial practices) that are applied to the forest landscape (AFCSSC, 1997: 9). Without ef-fective controls it would not be possible to deter-mine whether observed changes were due to in-dustrial activities, natural local fluctuations, or ex-ternal influences such as climate change (Arcese and Sinclair, 1997). Protected areas, acting as eco-logical benchmarks in which natural processes are maintained, are able to act as such controls, and this constitutes a second major role for these ar-eas (Sinclair, 1998).

Ecological benchmarks are primarily required for the detection of changes at the landscape and regional scales. The issues of concern include most of the limitations of the NDM listed previ-ously (e.g., the impact of fragmentation, access, representation of old growth, etc.). Evaluation efforts should include the monitoring of forest structure and pattern as well as selected indica-tors of biodiversity and ecological processes (Sch-neider, 1997). Indicators should facilitate the evaluation of the cumulative effects of industrial activities as this is a key role for benchmarks (AFMSC, 1997: 11). For stand-level issues (e.g., regeneration rates, coarse woody debris, etc.), ecological benchmarks would provide important information on the interaction between land-scape-level effects and stand-level processes. Small permanent sample plots imbedded in the indus-trial land base would also be useful for stand-level monitoring because they can be easily replicated and spatially matched to specific management areas.

Although the adaptive management ap-proach significantly augments the ability of the NDM to achieve its objectives, it should not be expected that it will resolve all problems that oc-cur as a consequence of industrial activities. A variety of barriers typically hamper the success-ful application of adaptive management, includ-ing the complexity of the natural systems being managed, time lags between cause and effect, economic and logistical constraints, and institu-tional and political factors (Walters, 1997). In a review of 25 adaptive management initiatives, Walters (1997) found that 18 did not proceed beyond the initial planning stages, and most of the others were inadequately planned.

Conservation of Wilderness

Although the public clearly understands and ap-preciates the economic benefits flowing from Canada's forests, this is not what they feel is most important to them when presented with a direct comparison of benefits (Corporate Research As-sociates, 1997: 8). Canadians are most likely to value forests for ecological benefits (such as protecting water, air and soil), providing habitat for wildlife, and wilderness preservation (Fig. 7.2). When surveyed, 77% of Albertans expressed an interest in participating in outdoor activities in natural areas (EC, 1999: 41), 58% favoured curtailing access of resource companies to wilderness lands (Angus Reid Group, 1994), and 93% thought it important to protect examples of the full range of Alberta's landscapes and wildlife by setting aside wildland areas where there is no industrial activity (Dunvegan Group Ltd., 1994). The public demand for the preservation of wilderness, which by definition implies the prohibition of industrial activities and associated road-building, constitutes a third role for protected areas in northern Alberta.

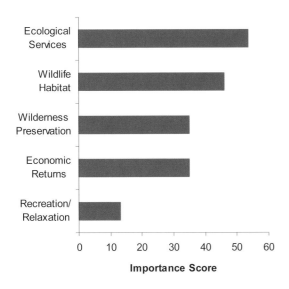

Fig. 7.2. Importance of forest values held by Canadians in 1997. Scores range from 0 (least important) to 100 (most important). Source: Corporate Research Associates, 1997: 36.

Research

Although there has been a substantial increase in research on boreal systems over the past decade, our knowledge of forest ecosystems remains little more than rudimentary. Much study, over an extended period of time, will be required before we can claim to understand the processes that we are attempting to emulate with the NDM. Unfortunately, as the natural landscape becomes fragmented and modified by road building and resource extraction, it will become progressively more difficult to find study areas in which to investigate natural processes. Consequently, protected areas will take on an increasingly important role as study areas for future research initiatives. In the words of Maser (1990), "Natural areas are the parts catalogs and the maintenance manuals not only for that which *is*, but also for that which can *be*."

Design Considerations

Representation

Protected areas maintain biodiversity by maintaining the habitat and ecosystem processes that species require for their existence (Noss, 1992). However, the habitat requirements of most species are not known (in fact, most species have not even been described). For this reason, among others, a species by species approach to habitat conservation is unworkable (Franklin, 1993). The alternative, termed the "coarse-filter" approach, attempts to meet the habitat requirements of the majority of species by ensuring that the full spectrum of ecosystem types is represented within the system of protected areas (Noss, 1992; Kavanagh and Iacobelli, 1995: 10).

The distribution of major ecosystem types in Alberta is provided by the Natural Regions and

Subregions classification developed by the provincial government (see Fig. 1.6). This system of classification delineates ecosystems on the basis of differences in geology, landforms, soils, hydrology, climate, and dominant vegetation patterns (AEP, 1994a: 2). For a system of protected areas to be fully representative, protected areas should be established within each Natural Subregion (AEP, 1994b: 2).

In addition to broad-scale representation, protected areas need to provide representation of smaller-scale landscape features (e.g., riparian zones, bogs, etc.). A report produced as part of the Special Places 2000 initiative identifies the key landscape features that should be considered and summarizes (by Natural Subregion) the area of each that is represented in existing protected areas (AEP, 1994b: 26).

Representation is also a factor in the selection of areas to be used as ecological benchmarks (AFMSC, 1997: 11). To provide the greatest statistical power in detecting changes due to industrial practices, benchmark areas should be matched to major resource management units (e.g., FMAs) in terms of ecological composition and spatial proximity.

Ecological Integrity

Representation of ecosystems and landscape features is only the first step in protected area design. Representation alone cannot ensure that natural processes will be maintained or that native species will survive (Noss, 1995: 6). Thus, a complementary goal to adequate representation is the maintenance of ecological integrity. Ecological integrity is defined as the degree to which all ecosystem components and their interactions are represented and functioning (Quigley et al., 1996: 29).

A fundamental requirement for the maintenance of ecological integrity within protected areas is the maintenance of disturbance-renewal cycles (Noss, 1992). Fire is the dominant disturbance agent in the boreal forest and is responsible for much of the structure, pattern, and ultimately biodiversity, present in boreal landscapes (see Chapter 6). It follows that a key design consideration for protected areas in northern Alberta is the maintenance of a natural fire regime.

Several researchers have suggested that protected areas must be substantially larger than the largest disturbance for the natural fire regime to be maintained (Pickett and Thompson, 1978; White, 1987; Baker, 1992). In a computer simulation study using historical fire data from northern Alberta I determined that protected areas of 5000 km^2 had a high probability of maintaining stable rates of burning, with full representation of the natural range of fire sizes (Schneider, 2000). The implication is that all forest age classes and patch sizes will continue to be represented (though not necessarily in a steady state). In contrast, burning in protected areas of 500 km^2 was highly variable, generally resulting in either inadequate or excessive amounts of burning relative to what is required to maintain full representation of forest age classes and patch sizes over ecologically relevant periods of time (Schneider, 2000). These findings imply that in northern Alberta protected areas approaching or exceeding 5000 km^2 are required for maintaining fire regimes and, by extension, ecological integrity.

Limiting the use of fire suppression within protected areas and implementing prescriptive burns would help ensure that fires continue to be represented within protected areas (Richards et al., 1999). Buffer zones around the protected areas could be used to prevent fires from burning into the surrounding commercial forest. The restriction of fire suppression may not be possible during periods of extreme weather conditions, because of the risks associated with large uncontrollable fires. However, this caveat may ultimately not be of great importance, given the limited effectiveness of fire suppression when conditions are extreme (Johnson et al., 1998).

Other natural processes, such as nutrient cycling, forest succession, hydrological cycles, and so on, can be maintained within protected areas simply by limiting human interference. This can be achieved by (1) prohibiting industrial activities and the development of new access routes, (2) placing limits on motorized activities, and (3) design that incorporates a large core area and a buffer zone (Noss, 1992). Hunting and trapping of game species need not be prohibited if the viability and ecological role of all species can be maintained through careful regulation. The acceptability of hunting and trapping must be determined on a species by species and site by site basis (Kavanagh and Iacobelli, 1995: 20). Boundaries must be permanent (i.e., legislated) to ensure that natural processes are maintained indefinitely (Kavanagh and Iacobelli, 1995: 21).

Connectivity

The boreal forest is structured as a mosaic of patches that differ in vegetation type, age, size, and other attributes (see Chapter 6). Consequently, for most species the landscape is comprised of islands of optimal habitat within a matrix of suboptimal or unsuitable habitat (Knight and Morris, 1996). The spatial distribution of these islands is different for each species, reflecting the unique habitat requirements of each (Fig. 7.3). For species with small home ranges, movement among habitat islands is necessary for ba-

sic population processes such as juvenile dispersal and mating. For species that are more mobile, movement among patches is a common part of foraging behaviour (Taylor et al., 1993). Connectivity among patches will be highest within protected areas because they are designed to maintain natural patterns and processes and have few human-made barriers to movement.

There is a general consensus among researchers that populations of a few thousand individuals are required for the long-term viability of most species, and even more for species that exhibit wide fluctuations in population size (Soule, 1987; Thomas, 1990; Nunney and Campbell, 1993). This is because small isolated populations are prone to the loss of genetic variability and to extreme fluctuations in size, both of which increase the probability of extinction (Gilpin, 1987). Protected areas that are designed to maintain ecologi-

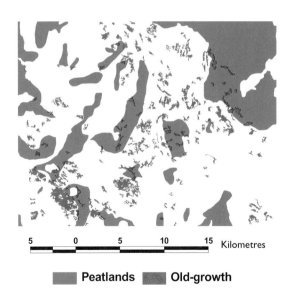

5   0   5   10   15   Kilometres

◼ **Peatlands** ◼ **Old-growth**

Fig. 7.3. Distribution of patches of peat and forest greater than 100 years in a 625 km² region north of Lac la Biche. (Map: Forest Watch Alberta)

cal integrity (i.e., several thousand square kilometres in size) should be capable of providing both the habitat and connectivity needs of viable populations of most native species in a given Natural Subregion (even if habitat availability is altered by large disturbances). The alternative approach of establishing several smaller protected areas is less preferable to a single large protected area per Subregion, even if the area and habitat representation are equal, because it implies greater reliance on the industrial landscape for connectivity.

Some species have such large area requirements that viable populations cannot be achieved in individual protected areas, even if they are several thousand square kilometres in size (Table 7.1). Many of these wide-ranging species have important ecological roles and their presence is critical for maintaining ecological integrity (Noss et al., 1996). Consequently, a system of protected areas must be designed to facilitate the movement of individuals among sites so that viable populations of all species can be achieved in the system as a whole (Noss, 1992). Connectivity among protected areas is also required to facilitate the movement of species in response to climate change (see below).

Facilitating the movement of individuals among protected areas is difficult in a boreal setting because of the vast distances involved. Assuming that an emphasis is placed on establish-

Table 7.1. Estimated area required for 1000 individuals of wide-ranging boreal species.

Species	Density/Home Range (km^2)[1]	Area for 1000 Individuals (km^2)[2]	Source[3]
Marten	2.3 (HR: females)	1150	Powell, 1994
Pileated woodpecker	4.1 (HR: pair)	2050	Bull and Holthausen, 1993
Black bear	7.5 (HR: females)	3750	Fuller and Keith, 1980a
Moose	4.0 (D)	4000	Schneider and Wasel, 2000
Great-horned owl	9-16 (D)	12,500	Rusch et al., 1972
Fisher	27.8 (HR: females)	13,900	Pinsonneault et al., 1997
Goshawk	15-50 (HR: pair)	16,250	Schaffer et al., 1996
Lynx	3.3-33.3 (D)	18,300	Poole, 1994
Grizzly bear	33-50 (D)	41,500	Mace and Waller, 1997
Wolverine	105 (HR: females)	52,500	Whitman et al., 1986
Wolf	90-158 (D)	124,000	Fuller and Keith, 1980b
Caribou	711 (HR)	several thousand[4]	Stuart-Smith et al., 1997

[1]Density (D) listed if available (animals per km^2), otherwise home range (HR) is listed (total area, in km^2).
[2]Area = Density*1000. For species for which density is unknown a crude estimate of the area is calculated as: Mean Home Range/2*1000 (assuming that female territories cover the entire landscape, without overlap, and that the number of males is equal to the number of females).
[3]Data from Alberta, unless unavailable.
[4]Because caribou exist in herds their density cannot be determined from home range estimates.

ing large protected areas (to maintain ecological integrity) and that sites are located in different Natural Subregions (to attain adequate representation) the minimum distance between major sites will be on the order of 100 km, with the exception of sites adjacent to Wood Buffalo National Park. Furthermore, dispersal patterns will be not be dictated by the location of the nearest protected area (which will be unknown to individuals) but by local habitat availability. Therefore, movement between sites will generally not occur in a single episode, but over a period of years, even for wide-ranging species (Harrison, 1992).

To facilitate movement between sites, special management of the intervening landscape will be required (Noss, 1992). Animals will have to reside in these special management zones for extended periods; therefore, the zones will need to provide high-quality habitat and be wide enough to fully accommodate the territory size requirements of wide-ranging species (i.e., many kilometres) (Harrison, 1992). Barriers to movement must be minimized by setting low thresholds for road density, prohibiting intensive forestry operations, and the use of low-impact practices by the petroleum industry. The rate of forest harvesting must be relatively low and operations must strictly adhere to the NDM. Initially, the special management zones will differ little from the surrounding landscape and, therefore, will receive little preferential use. However, their effectiveness as movement corridors will steadily increase as the cumulative impact of industrial use of the surrounding landscape increases.

Ecological Benchmark Areas

In addition to their role in maintaining biodiversity, sites designed according the aforementioned

criteria will also effectively serve as ecological benchmarks. The maintenance of natural ecological processes in these areas will provide an appropriate contrast to changes observed on the industrial land base (Sinclair, 1998). Furthermore, the sites will be large enough to provide statistically robust measurements of biodiversity indicators, including those applicable to large-scale phenomena (e.g., cumulative impacts).

An additional design consideration for ecological benchmarks is location. Benchmark areas should be located as near to major regions of industrial activity as possible and should include upland forests that are the focus of forest industry activities, while maintaining representation of Natural Subregions.

It is sometimes argued that the lack of truly pristine areas in northern Alberta invalidates the benchmark concept. However, benchmark areas that have had some human impact will still provide a very strong contrast with the industrial land base, which is ultimately what determines their usefulness. This contrast will increase as industrial impacts accumulate over time and will be critical for providing early warning of problems associated with industrial activities (Sinclair, 1998).

Climate Change

Recent climate models predict that the western Canadian interior will warm by several degrees as a consequence of increased levels of CO_2 and other greenhouse gases (Hogg and Hurdle, 1995). The increased CO_2 and temperature are expected to increase forest productivity, lengthen growing seasons, alter disturbance regimes, and change patterns of precipitation (Burton and Cumming, 1995; Hogg and Hurdle, 1995). As a consequence of these changes vegetation patterns within protected areas may change and animal species may need to shift their range in order to maintain viability (Graham, 1988).

To accommodate the potential impacts of climate change, the system of protected areas should be designed to maximize the diversity of landforms, ensure broad geographic representation, and incorporate redundancy (Halpin, 1997). In this way individual sites will always be able to maintain a diverse mix of species, even if the composition of habitat and the distribution of species changes over time (Halpin, 1997). It is essential that connectivity among protected areas be maintained so that species are able to track their preferred habitat (Graham, 1988).

Implementation

In the following sections I develop a framework for a system of protected areas in northern Alberta designed to help maintain biodiversity and function as ecological benchmarks. Although the proposed protected areas will help preserve wilderness in northern Alberta, public demand for wilderness preservation is difficult to quantify and, therefore, is not explicitly incorporated in the framework. Public demand for additional preservation of wilderness may arise in future years.

Existing Protected Areas

In 2001, the Special Places 2000 program, that was intended to complete the protected area system in Alberta, was concluded (AEP, 1995). Unfortunately, the selection of sites was based almost entirely on the representation of landscape features and the minimization of conflict with existing industrial users (AEP, 1994b: 2). Neither the maintenance of ecological integrity, the connectivity needs of wide-ranging species, nor the

role of protected areas as benchmarks were utilized as design criteria. Despite acknowledgement by Alberta Environment that: "*large wilderness areas in the order of 4000 km² and larger are recommended for complete biodiversity and wilderness protection*" (AEP, 1994b: 2), only one site of this size was established (the Caribou Mountain Wildland). Finally, existing industrial dispositions were maintained in the new parks, making it questionable whether these sites are protected in any real sense.

With the conclusion of Special Places 2000, 12.8% of Alberta is now under some form of protection (Fig. 7.4). In northern Alberta, 14.0% is protected. However, these figures belie an significant imbalance in representation. Most of the area protected is in the Rocky Mountain parks and in Wood Buffalo National Park (WBNP). Many of the other Natural Regions are not adequately represented in the system (Fig. 7.5). Furthermore, very little of the area protected is representative of the merchantable forest that has been allocated to the forest industry. Finally, most of the parks in northern Alberta are not large enough to adequately maintain ecological integrity (Fig. 7.6).

Establishment of Core Protected Areas

Additional large core reserves distributed among the Natural Subregions of northern Alberta are required to address the design considerations presented earlier. Large size (i.e., in the range of 5000 km²) is necessary to ensure that the sites are capable of maintaining ecological integrity, which is in turn required for the maintenance of biodiversity and the use of sites for scientific study and as benchmarks. Large size is also required to ensure that viable populations of most native species can be maintained without dependence on

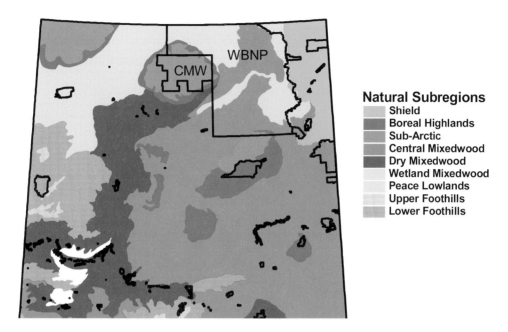

Fig. 7.4. Protected areas (outlined in black) in northern Alberta in 2001, superimposed on a map of Natural Subregions. WBNP = Wood Buffalo National Park; CMW = Caribou Mountains Wildland. Source: AE, 2001

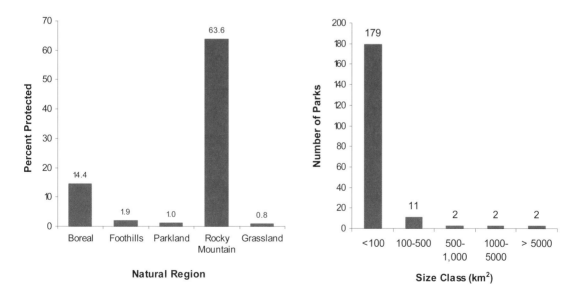

Fig. 7.5. Percent of area protected in 2001, by Natural Region. Source: AE, 2001.

Fig. 7.6. Number of protected areas in northern Alberta in 2001, by size class. Source: AE, 2001.

the industrial landscape for connectivity. Finally, large size is required to enable adequate sampling in the context of benchmark areas.

The requirement for multiple core reserves reflects the need to (1) represent all ecosystem types, (2) ensure wide geographic distribution to facilitate recolonization of the industrial land base, if required, (3) facilitate the matching of benchmark areas to regions of high industrial use, and (4) incorporate redundancy into the system to accommodate climate change and unforeseen changes. Although the Central Mixedwood Subregion is represented in WBNP, at least one other large core area is warranted in this Subregion given that it constitutes almost one quarter of Alberta (AEP, 1994b: 26). Furthermore, most of Alberta's oil sands development, along with considerable conventional oil and gas activity and several forestry operations, are located in the southern half of the Central Mixedwood (AEP, 1998: 84). Consequently, there is a substantial need for a biodiversity reserve and ecological benchmark in this region.

The placement of the core protected areas requires consideration of the following factors (Noss, 1995: 1; AEP, 1998: 217):

- natural Subregion representation;
- representation of smaller-scale landforms;
- level of existing disturbance and road density;
- proximity to WBNP;
- potential for supplying habitat for rare or endangered species;
- incorporation of areas of high species richness; and
- minimization of conflict with existing industrial commitments.

With the exception of the Central Mixedwood Subregion, the optimal placement of sites, based on the above criteria, is readily apparent (Fig. 7.7). More than one potential site exists in the southern half of the Central Mixedwood (AEP, 1998, Fig. 50), and the two most likely candidates are shown in Fig. 7.7. Because there is minimal industrial activity in the Shield Natural Region, a large core area is not a priority for this Region. The delineation of actual boundaries is beyond the scope of this paper, but in general, emphasis should be placed on maximizing habitat diversity and ecological function (Noss, 1992). Because the sites are intended to be permanent, a long-term perspective is important, implying that landform diversity should be emphasized over transitory features such as old-growth or pre-existing human disturbance (Kavanagh and Iacobelli, 1995: 11).

Even if the large core reserves are several thousand square kilometres in size they will not be able to capture all of the ecological diversity of northern Alberta. Additional protected areas of smaller size (100-1000 km^2) will be needed to represent unique localized landscape features (e.g., sand dune complexes), areas of particularly high diversity (e.g., major river corridors), and the specialized habitat needs of rare or endangered species. These supplemental sites are intended to meet the habitat requirements of a select group of species, in contrast to the coarse-filter objectives of the large core sites. The locations of most of these supplemental sites have been identified through the Special Places 2000 program (AEP, 1996b: 8-15; AEP, 1998: 236-267). Given the limited objectives of the program, not all sites were established and the size of many sites is inadequate.

The protected area system in northern Alberta must also incorporate corridors and buffers. The nature and management of corridors have been described earlier, and in general, the

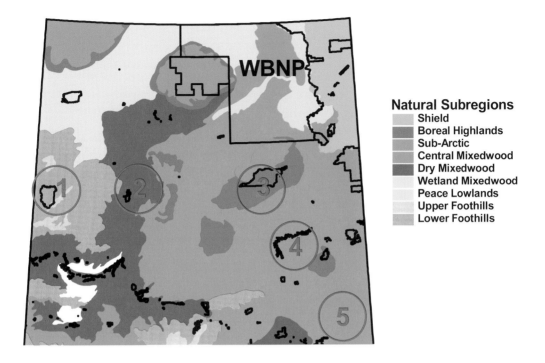

Fig. 7.7. Candidate locations for additional large core protected areas. Each area is 5000 km², drawn approximately to scale. Criteria used to select the sites are described in the text. Existing sites are outlined in black.

characteristics of buffer zones should be similar. Harvesting operations within buffer zones could occur at a low rate, with strict adherence to the NDM. Allocations would have to be based on the understanding that limited fire suppression would be practiced within the protected area, presenting a potentially higher risk of fire in the buffer zone. The size of buffers would be based on the nature and intensity of the industrial activities occurring outside protected areas and on the sensitivity of key species to these activities.

The protected area framework presented here is based on minimum requirements for representation and integrity necessary for the maintenance of biodiversity. The four core areas, at 5000 km² each, would add 4.9% to the 14.0% of northern Alberta that is currently protected (as of 2001). With the addition of supplemental sites required for the protection of unique landscape features and habitat types the total area of protection is in the same range as the 20% target that the Senate Sub-Committee on the Boreal Forest (1999) suggested is appropriate for the boreal forest.

The management of protected areas, once established, should focus on the maintenance of ecological integrity (Sinclair, 1998; PEICNP, 2000). As fundamental principles, the boundaries of the sites must be permanent (through legislation) and all industrial use must be prohibited (Kavanagh and Iacobelli, 1995: 20). In addition, access and motorized activities should be minimized, and natural disturbances should be permitted to occur (at least in the large core reserves) (Noss, 1992). Further management prescriptions will be largely site-specific. The report released by Parks Canada on the ecological integrity of Canada's national parks provides useful guidance (PEICNP, 2000).

Floating Reserves

The concept of so-called "floating reserves" has occasionally been proposed as an alternative to a system of permanent protected areas. The intent is to maximize the utilization of the landscape for resource extraction while still providing some protection. Industrial use is restricted in defined areas for a specified period of time (e.g., 50 or 100 years), and this land is then brought back into production in exchange for new reserves.

As an alternative for permanent protected areas, floating reserves are not a serious consideration. The obvious problem is that after the first rotation of sites, the "new" reserves will be incapable of fulfilling any of the core objectives of protected areas. They will not be repositories of natural ecological processes acting as safeguards for maintaining biodiversity, they will not be capable of acting as benchmarks by providing a contrast to other industrial areas, and they will not be considered as wilderness by the public.

Floating reserves could, however, play an important role in the maintenance of old-growth forest within the *industrial* land base. The maintenance of older forest stands on the landscape, in natural patterns of quantity, patch size, and distribution, is a central tenet of the NDM (Niemela, 1999). This application of floating reserves is discussed in the next chapter.

Literature Cited

AE (Alberta Environment). 2001. Parks and protected areas, on-line database. (Available at: http://www.cd.gov.ab.ca)

AEP (Alberta Environmental Protection). 1994a. Natural Regions of Alberta. Alberta Environmental Protection, Edmonton, AB.

AEP (Alberta Environmental Protection). 1994b. Alberta protected areas system analysis. Alberta Environmental Protection, Edmonton, AB.

AEP (Alberta Environmental Protection). 1995. Special Places 2000: Alberta's natural heritage. Alberta Environmental Protection, Edmonton, AB.

AEP (Alberta Environmental Protection). 1996a. The status of Alberta's timber supply. (Available at: www.gov.ab.ca/env/forests.html)

AEP (Alberta Environmental Protection). 1996b. Selecting protected areas: the Foothills Natural Region of Alberta. Alberta Environmental Protection, Edmonton, AB.

AEP (Alberta Environmental Protection). 1998. The boreal forest Natural Region of Alberta. Alberta Environmental Protection, Edmonton, AB.

AFCSSC (Alberta Forest Conservation Strategy Steering Committee). 1997. Alberta forest conservation strategy. Alberta Environmental Protection, Edmonton, AB. (Available at: www.borealcentre.ca/reports/reports.html)

AFMSC (Alberta Forest Management Science Council). 1997. Sustainable forest management and its major elements. Report prepared for Alberta Environmental Protection, Edmonton, AB. (Available at: www.borealcentre.ca/reports/reports.html)

Angus Reid Group. 1994. Canadians and the Environment. Alberta Environmental Protection memorandum. Edmonton, Alberta.

Arcese, P. and A. R. E. Sinclair. 1997. The role of protected areas as ecological baselines. J.Wildl. Mgmt. 61:587-602.

Armstrong, G. 1999. A stochastic characterization of the natural disturbance regime of Alberta's boreal forest: a simple process producing complex outcomes. Can. J. For. Res. 29:424-433.

Armstrong, G., S. Cumming, and W. Adamowicz. 1999. Timber supply implications of natural disturbance management. For. Chron. 75:497-504.

Baker, W. 1992. The landscape ecology of large disturbances in the design and management of nature reserves. Land. Ecol. 7:181-194.

Bull, E. L. and R. S. Holthausen. 1993. Habitat use and management of pileated woodpeckers in northeastern Oregon. J. Wildl. Manage. 57:335-345.

Burton, P. and S. Cumming. 1995. Potential effects of climatic change on some western Canadian forests, based on phenological enhancements to a patch model of forest succession. Water, Air and Soil Poll. 82:401-414.

Corporate Research Associates. 1997. Tracking survey of Canadian attitudes towards natural resources issues, 1997. Natural Resources Canada, Ottawa, ON. (Available at www.nrcan.gc.ca/homepage/tracking.shtml)

Cumming, S. 2001. Forest type and wildfire in the Alberta boreal mixedwood: what do fires burn? Ecol. Appl. 11: 97-110.

Cumming, S. and G. Armstrong. 1999. Divided land bases and overlapping tenures in Alberta's boreal forests: a simulation study of policy alternatives. Working Paper 1999-3, Sustainable Forest Management Network, Edmonton, AB. (Available at: http://sfm-1.biology.ualberta.ca/english/home/index.htm)

Cumming, S., P. Burton, and B. Klinkenberg. 1996. Boreal mixedwood forests may have no "representative" regions: some implications for reserve design. Ecography 19:162-180.

Cumming, S., F. Schmiegelow, and P. Burton. 2000. Gap dynamics in boreal aspen stands: is the forest older than we think? Ecol Appl. 10:744-759.

Dunvegan Group Limited. 1994. Special Places 2000. Opinion poll prepared for the World Wildlife Fund, Canada. Toronto, Ontario.

EC (Environment Canada). 1995. Canadian biodiversity strategy. Environment Canada, Hull, PQ.

EC (Environment Canada). 1999. The importance of nature to Canadians: survey highlights. Environment Canada, Ottawa, ON. (Available at: www.ec.gc.ca/nature/survey.htm)

Franklin, J. 1993. Preserving biodiversity: species, ecosystems, or landscapes? Ecol. Appl. 3:202-205.

Fuller, T. and L. Keith. 1980a. Summer ranges, cover-type use, and denning of black bears near Fort McMurray, Alberta. Can. Field Nat. 94:80-83.

Fuller, T. K. and L. B. Keith. 1980b. Wolf population dynamics and prey relationships in northeastern Alberta. J. Wildl. Manage. 44:583-602.

Gilpin, M. E. 1987. Spatial structure and population vulnerability. Pages 125-140 in Soule, M. E., editor. Viable populations for conservation. Cambridge University Press, Cambridge, England.

Graham, R. W. 1988. The role of climatic change in the design of biological reserves: the paleoecological perspective for conservation biology. Cons. Biol. 2:391-394.

Gunderson, L. 1999. Resilience, flexibility and adaptive management - - antidotes for spurious certitude? Cons. Ecol., 3. (Available at: www.consecol.org/vol3/iss1/art7)

Halpin, P. N. 1997. Global climate change and natural-area protection: management responses and research directions. Ecol. Appl. 7:828-843.

Harrison, R. 1992. Toward a theory of inter-refuge corridor design. Cons. Biol. 6:293-295.

Hogg, E. and P. Hurdle. 1995. The aspen parkland in western Canada: a dry-climate analogue for the future boreal forest? Water, Air and Soil Poll. 82:391-400.

Hunter, M. L. 1993. Natural fire regimes as spatial models for managing boreal forests. Biol. Cons. 72:115-120.

Johnson, E. A., K. Miyanishi, and J. M. H. Weir. 1998. Wildfires in the western Canadian boreal forest: landscape patterns and ecosystem management. J. Veg. Sci. 9:603-610.

Kavanagh, K. and T. Iacobelli. 1995. A protected areas gap analysis methodology: planning for the conservation of biodiversity. World Wildlife Fund, Toronto, ON.

Keenan, R. and J. Kimmins. 1993. The ecological effects of clear-cutting. Environ. Rev. 1:121-144.

Knight, T. and D. Morris. 1996. How many habitats do landscapes contain? Ecology 77: 1756-1764.

Lieffers, V. and J. Beck. 1994. A semi-natural approach to mixedwood management in the prairie provinces. For. Chron. 70:260-264.

Mace, R. D. and J. S. Waller. 1997. Spatial and temporal interaction of male and female grizzly bears in northwestern Montana. J. Wildl. Manage. 61:39-52.

Maser, C. 1990. On the "naturalness" of natural areas: a perspective for the future. Nat. Areas J. 10:129-133.

Murphy, E. C. and W. A. Lehnhausen. 1998. Density and foraging ecology of woodpeckers following a stand-replacement fire. J. Wildl. Manage. 62:1359-1372.

Niemela, J. 1999. Management in relation to disturbance in the boreal forest. For. Ecol. Manage. 115:127-134.

Noss, R. 1992. The wildlands project: land conservation strategy. Wild Earth 1:10-25.

Noss, R. 1995. Maintaining ecological integrity in representative reserve networks. World Wildlife Fund, Toronto, ON.

Noss, R., H. Quigley, M. Hornocker, T. Merrill, and P. Paquet. 1996. Conservation biology and carnivore conservation in the Rocky Mountains. Cons. Biol. 10:949-963.

Nunney, L. and K. A. Campbell. 1993. Assessing minimum viable population size: demography meets population genetics. Trends Ecol. Evol. 8:234-239.

PEICNP (Panel on the Ecological Integrity of Canada's National Parks). 2000. Final report of the panel on the ecological integrity of Canada's national parks. Parks Canada, Ottawa, ON. (Available at: www.parkscanada. gc.ca/ ei-ie/index_e.html)

Pickett, S. and J. N. Thompson. 1978. Patch dynamics and the design of nature reserves. Biol. Cons. 13:27-37.

Pinsonneault, Y., L. D. Roy, and B. E. Grover. 1997. Winter habitat use by fishers (Martes pennanti) in harvested and unharvested forests, northeast Alberta. Alberta Research Centre, Vegreville, AB.

Poole, K. G. 1994. Characteristics of an unharvested lynx population during a snowshoe hare decline. J. Wildl. Manage. 58:608-618.

Powell, R. 1994. Structure and spacing of Martes populations. Pages 101-121 in Buskirk, S., A. Harestad, M. Raphael, and R. Powell, editors. Martens, sables, and fishers: biology and conservation. Cornell University Press, Ithaca, NY.

Quigley, T. M., R. W. Haynes, and R. T. Graham. 1996. Integrated scientific assessment for ecosystem management in the interior Columbia basin and portions of the Klamath and Great Basins. U.S. Forest Service, Pacific Northwest Research Station, Gen. Tech. Rep. PNW-GTR-382., Portland, OR. (Available at: www.icbemp. gov/)

Reed, R., J. Johnson-Barnard, and W. Baker. 1996. Contribution of roads to forest fragmentation in the Rocky Mountains. Cons. Biol. 10:1098-1106.

Richards, S., H. Possingham, and J. Tizard. 1999. Optimal fire management for maintaining community diversity. Ecol. Appl. 9:880-892.

Rusch, D. H., E. C. Meslow, P. D. Doerr, and L. B. Keith. 1972. Response of great horned owl populations to changing prey densities. J. Wildl. Manage. 36:282-296.

Schaffer, W., B. Beck, J. Beck, R. Bonar, and L. Hunt. 1996. Northern goshawk breeding habitat. Pages 175-186 in Beck, B., J. Beck, J. Bessie, R. Bonar, and M. Todd, editors. Habitat suitability index models for 35 wildlife species in the Foothills Model Forest. Foothills Model Forest, Hinton, AB.

Schneider, R. R. 1997. Ecological diversity monitoring framework. Foothills Model Forest, Hinton, AB. (Available at www.fmf.ab.ca/bm/fw.htm)

Schneider, R. R. 2000. Maintaining a natural fire regime within protected areas. Alberta Centre for Boreal Research, Edmonton, AB. (Available at: www.borealcentre. ca/reports/reports.html)

Schneider, R. R. and S. Wasel. 2000. The effect of human settlement on the density of moose in northern Alberta. J. Wildl. Manage. 64:513-520.

Senate Subcommittee on the Boreal Forest. 1999. Competing realities: the boreal forest at risk. The Senate of Canada, Ottawa, ON. (Available at: www.parl.gc.ca/36/ 1/parlbus/commbus/senate/com-e/rep-e.htm)

Sinclair, A. R. E. 1998. Natural regulation of ecosystems in protected areas as ecological baselines. Wildl. Soc. Bull. 26:399-409.

Soule, M. 1987. Where do we go from here? Pages 175-183 in Soule, M., editor. Viable populations for conservation. Cambridge University Press, Cambridge, England.

Stuart-Smith, K., C. Bradshaw, S. Boutin, D. Hebert, and B. Rippin. 1997. Woodland caribou relative to landscape patterns in northeastern Alberta. J. Wildl. Manage. 61:622-633.

Taylor, P., L. Fahrig, K. Henein, and G. Merriam. 1993. Connectivity is a vital element of landscape structure. Oikos 68:571-573.

Thomas, C. D. 1990. What do real population dynamics tell us about minimum viable population sizes. Cons. Biol. 4:324-327.

Trombulak, S. and C. Frissell. 2000. Review of ecological effects of roads on terrestrial and aquatic communities. Cons. Biol. 14:18-30.

Walters, C. 1997. Challenges in adaptive management of riparian and coastal ecosystems. Cons. Ecol. 1. (Available at: www.consecol.org/vol1/iss2/art1)

Walters, C. and C. Holling. 1990. Large-scale management experiments and learning by doing. Ecology 71:2060-2068.

White, P. 1987. Natural disturbance, patch dynamics, and landscape pattern in natural areas. Nat. Areas J. 7:14-22.

Whitman, J. S., W. B. Ballard, and C. L. Gardner. 1986. Home range and habitat use by wolverines in southcentral Alaska. J. Wildl. Manage. 50:460-463.

Xu, J., P. Yeung, and P. Lee. 1999. Comparison of soil nutrients between wildfire and harvest stands. Pages 30-55 in Lee, P., editor. Fire and harvest residual project: the impact of wildfire and harvest residuals on forest structure and biodiversity in aspen-dominated boreal forests of Alberta. Alberta Research Council, Vegreville, AB.

8. Old-Growth

Old-growth forests are unique in terms of their structure and ecological processes. Consequently, the maintenance of old growth is critical to the maintenance of forest biodiversity. In this chapter I review the status of old-growth in Alberta, including a discussion of dynamics (origin and loss) and an assessment of current quantity and distribution. In the concluding section I discuss management options for maintaining old-growth and the biodiversity associated with it.

The focus of this chapter is on the management of old-growth forests occurring within the industrial land base. Black spruce and larch, which are generally not targeted for harvesting in Alberta, are not included in the analysis or discussion.

General Ecology of Old-Growth

Defining Characteristics

The unifying feature of old-growth is not age per se, but the set of characteristics shared by most forest types in the later stages of succession. A key feature is breakup of the canopy due to the mortality of individual trees as they reach maturity (Burton et al.,1999). This process in turn leads to the release of understory plants, accumulation of snags and downed logs, and in some cases, the emergence of secondary canopy species (Stelfox, 1995: *v*). Relative to younger stages, old stands have trees of many ages

119

and sizes and have more large canopy trees, large snags, and large downed logs (Burton et al., 1999; Lee et al., 2000). Overall, structural diversity is highest in old stands, and this is reflected in unique plant and animal communities as well as high overall species richness, relative to younger stands (Stelfox, 1995: *vi*; Timoney, 2001).

A Working Definition

Although it would be preferable to identify old-growth stands directly on the basis of the previously described structural criteria, timber inventories do not contain the required attributes. An alternative approach is to develop simple working definitions of old-growth based on known relationships between stand age and successional stage. Age-based definitions of old-growth must be defined separately for each stand type because tree species mature at different rates (Table 8.1). Also, it should be understood that age-based definitions provide only a coarse assessment of old-growth (Lee et al., 2000). There is substantial variability in the rate of stand development due to local variations in soil and climate, among other factors, and timber inventories are known to systematically underestimate the age of older stands (Cumming et al., 2000).

Table 8.1. Typical age at which old-growth characteristics are apparent, for commercial forest stand types in Alberta.

Forest Type	Old-Growth Age[1]
Deciduous	> 100
White spruce	> 140
Mixedwood[2]	> 100
Pine	> 120

[1]Adapted from Timoney, 2001.
[2]Mixture of coniferous and deciduous species.

Ecological Importance

Old-growth stands contribute to the maintenance of forest biodiversity in several ways. For some species, advanced tree age is itself a critical attribute. For example, plant species that require a long time for colonization and growth, such as lichens, are often found only in abundance in old-growth stands (Esseen et al., 1996). Cone-eating birds, such as the red crossbill, are dependent on the existence of old-growth because older coniferous trees produce many more cones much more consistently, and of greater size, than do younger trees (Benkman, 1993). Many species, including little brown bats and pileated woodpeckers, seek out the large old trees found in old-growth stands for foraging and roosting (Crampton and Barclay, 1998; McClelland and McClelland, 1999). Finally, the accumulation of large dead wood, characteristic of old-growth stands, supports unique assemblages of wood-decomposing species (Crites and Dale, 1995), as well as providing foraging opportunities and shelter for many other species (Lee et al., 1997).

In more general terms, the complex structure of old-growth provides a large variety of habitat types for exploitation by species with specialized requirements. Consequently, old-growth stands have the highest overall diversity of species, relative to other age classes, with representation of many rare species (Stelfox, 1995: *vi*). Furthermore, many species have their greatest abundance in old-growth. For example, Schieck and Nietfeld (1995) found that 21 of the 33 bird species they studied in the boreal mixedwood forest had their highest abundance in old-growth stands, and nine of those species were more than four times as abundant in old stands as in other ages. A number of bird species, such as the black-throated green warbler, brown creeper, and golden-crowned kinglet are essentially restricted to old-growth stands (Kirk et al., 1996). Similar patterns of diversity and abundance have been observed in mammalian communities (Roy et al., 1995), non-vascular plant communities (Crites and Dale, 1995), and wood-decomposing insects (Martikainen et al., 1999).

Natural Dynamics

Dynamics refers to the origin and loss of old-growth stands over time. In Alberta, most stands are initiated by fire, though insect damage can also be an initiating factor. Because fires in the boreal forest are relatively common, most patches of regenerating forest are re-burned before they actually reach old-growth status (Johnson et al., 1998). In stands that reach the old-growth stage (Table 8.1), the sporadic mortality of individual large mature trees produces gaps that are repopulated by new trees, enabling the stand to persist indefinitely (Kneeshaw and Bergeron, 1998; Cumming et al., 2000).

On upland sites (the focus of most northern forestry operations), white spruce and aspen usually regenerate together after fire, producing mixedwood stands (Lieffers et al., 1996). If white spruce growth is vigorous it will suppress the regeneration of new aspen, and the stand will become progressively dominated by white spruce. However, in many cases the recruitment of white spruce after fire is delayed because a source of seeds is not sufficiently close or because the fire was not hot enough to prepare a suitable seed bed, among other factors (Lieffers et al., 1996; Greene et al., 1999). The result is an increase in the length of time it takes to achieve spruce dominance — the so-called "extended mixedwood stage" (Cumming et al., 2000). For some stands multiple gen-

erations of spruce trees may be required before conifer dominance is achieved (Cumming et al., 2000). Consequently, the age of trees in white spruce stands will often underestimate the true age of the stand, sometimes by a large margin (Cumming et al., 2000).

The generation of white spruce stands through the extended mixedwood pathway requires that stands escape burning for very long periods. Under the current fire regime this might be an uncommon occurrence if all stand types had an equal probability of burning. However, recent research by Cumming (2000) has shown that the probability of burning in aspen stands is extremely low until the proportion of spruce exceeds approximately 50%.

Abundance and Distribution

Current Age Structure of the Forest

The only forest inventory providing provincial coverage is the Alberta Phase 3 inventory (Anonymous, 1985). Phase 3 inventory is based on aerial photography flown between 1970 and 1984. It is regularly updated by the Forest Service to account for forest harvesting and fires. The age of stands is estimated from known relationships between tree height and age, specific to each stand type, and limited field checking. The township location of each stand is recorded, permitting spatial analysis at the township scale.

The age structure of the forest derived from the Phase 3 inventory is generally consistent with our understanding of stand dynamics. Representation of deciduous stands declines markedly after 80 years, whereas white spruce stands only reach their peak at 140 years (Fig. 8.1). Given that aspen stands are relatively resistant to burning, this pattern is further evidence of the transition of stands from aspen to white spruce through the mixedwood stage.

A significant anomaly in the Phase 3 inventory is the relative paucity of stands in the 0-40 year age class (Fig. 8.1). There are two main reasons for this. First, there was a relatively low rate of fire in the 1960s and 1970s (see Fig. 6.2). Second, no new aerial surveys have been conducted since 1984; therefore, young regenerating stands have not been properly accounted for over the past two decades.

Using Phase 3 inventory and the definitions of old-growth listed in Table 8.1, 26.5% (by area) of commercial forest stands in Alberta are currently in the old-growth stage. The proportion of mixedwood stands in the old-growth stage is substantially greater than for either pure deciduous or pure white spruce stands (Fig. 8.2). This same pattern was described by Lee et al. (2000) in northeast Alberta using more detailed old-growth criteria and data derived from 1129 sample plots. The high proportion of old-growth among mixedwood stands is consistent with the stand dynamics described earlier. Old-growth characteristics are acquired early in these stands, due to the early mortality of aspen trees. In addition, the relatively fire-resistant extended mixedwood stage allows many stands to attain an advanced age before burning or converting to pure white spruce (Lee et al., 2000; Cumming, 2001).

For a variety of reasons the measures of old-growth presented in Fig. 8.2 represent minimum estimates. First, the criteria used to define old-growth were conservative. For example, although aspen stands often begin to acquire old-growth

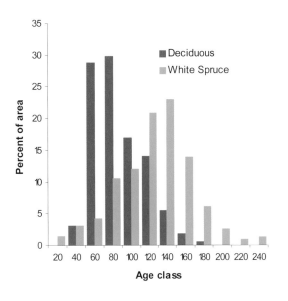

Fig. 8.1. The age structure of forest stands in Alberta, by stand type (denominator = total stand area, by type). Data from Phase 3 inventory current to 2000.

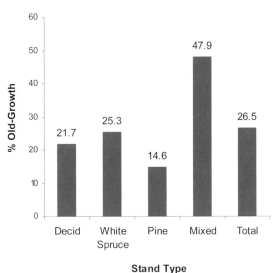

Fig. 8.2. Quantity of old-growth (as defined in Table 8.1), expressed as a percentage of the total stand area for each stand type. Data from Phase 3 inventory current to 2000.

characteristics by 85 years of age (Timoney, 2001), only stands greater than 100 years were included in the analysis. Second, as stands attain the uneven age structure characteristic of old-growth, it becomes increasingly difficult for photo-interpreters to accurately identify and age the trees that initiated the stand. This invariably leads to underestimation of the true age of older stands (Cumming et al., 2000). Furthermore, once the initiating cohort of trees dies, the photo-interpreted age of the stand will effectively become fixed, even though the stand may persist for many additional decades before burning. This applies particularly to aspen stands because they reach old-growth status quickly but are relatively resistant to burning (Cumming, 2001). It also applies to stands in the extended mixedwood pathway, and to pure spruce stands that were generated through the extended mixedwood pathway (Cumming et al., 2000).

Forest harvesting, which specifically targets old-growth stands (AEP, 1994a), is another factor resulting in underestimation of the proportion of old-growth naturally occurring on the landscape (Timoney, 2000). The greatest impact has been on white spruce, which has been harvested in Alberta, at increasing rates, for many decades. Some of the impact of harvesting may have been offset by fire suppression; however, available evidence suggests that such compensation has not been complete (see Chapter 6).

Another approach to the quantification of old-growth is to mathematically calculate (using probability theory) the expected proportion of old-growth on the basis of the rate of burning (Johnson and Van Wagner, 1985). Simply put, the greater the rate of fire, the more likely a stand will burn before reaching old age, and vice-versa. Given the average rate of burning in northern

Alberta since the provincial fire database was initiated in 1960 (0.4% per year), 57% of the forest should be greater than 140 years of age. Table 8.2 provides results for additional combinations of age at old growth and rate of burning. Overall, the amount of old-growth predicted on the basis of the rate of burning is substantially greater than the amount recorded in the Phase 3 inventory (Fig. 8.2), even if the rate of burning was substantially higher before we started keeping records. This is additional evidence that forest stands are older than the age of currently existing trees, and that our estimates of the amount of old-growth are quite conservative.

Spatial Distribution of Old-Growth

The distribution of old-growth is influenced by factors that affect the probability of burning, factors that affect regeneration, and an element of randomness. The probability of burning is affected by local topography, moisture regime, and climate, as well as transient factors such as stand type (Timoney, 2000; Cumming, 2001). Regeneration (particularly the determination of stand

Table 8.2. Expected percentage of area classified as old-growth when calculated from the average annual rate of burning.[1]

Old-Growth Age Criterion	Expected % Old-Growth[2]	
	Burn = 0.4%	Burn = 1%
> 100	67	37
> 120	62	30
> 140	57	25

[1]Results derived from the negative exponential function, which assumes random burning at a fixed rate (Johnson and Van Wagner, 1985).
[2]Expected percentage of landscape in old-growth given an annual rate of burn of 0.4% and 1%. Actual rate of burn recorded in northern Alberta: 1960-2000 = 0.40%; 1980-2000 = 0.63%. Source: ASRD, 2002.

type) is influenced by persistent factors such as soil type and moisture regime, and transient factors such as the availability of a seed source (Greene et al., 1999). Together, these various factors produce patterns in the distribution of old-growth that are apparent at different scales.

At the stand scale, particularly on the boreal plain, the basic pattern is set by the large but infrequent fires that are responsible for most burning (Johnson et al., 1998). These fires rejuvenate large regions of forest, producing a relatively even-aged forest matrix (Fig. 8.3). Within this matrix are islands of old-growth, representing trees that escaped burning, and islands of young forest, arising from the many small fires that occur each year (Fig. 8.3). The islands of old-growth are often downwind from water bodies and other fire-breaks, and so are generally not random in their distribution (Eberhart and Woodard, 1987; Fairbarns, 1991; Timoney, 2000). However, the ex-

act pattern changes from fire to fire because of differences in wind direction and other transient factors. As a general rule, the rate of fire increases with distance from a water body (Larsen, 1997). In the boreal forest the rate of burning is sufficiently high that it is rare for the matrix itself to reach old-growth status before being reburned (Johnson et al., 1998).

At the regional scale, additional patterns are apparent. In particular, there is a clear association between old-growth and large river corridors (Fig. 8.4). The abundance of old-growth within large river valleys reflects a low rate of burning relative to upland areas due to sloping banks that retard the advance of fire, increased moisture, and pres-

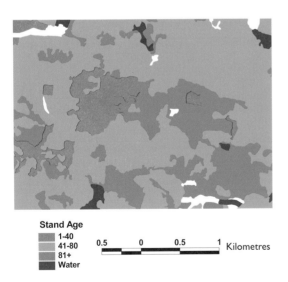

Stand Age
- 1-40
- 41-80
- 81+
- Water

0.5   0   0.5   1   Kilometres

Athabasca River
Clear-Cuts
Old-Growth

2   0   2   4   Kilometres

Fig. 8.3. Typical pattern of stand age structure in the boreal mixedwood forest. (Map: Forest Watch Alberta)

Fib. 8.4. Distribution of old-growth forest (> 100 years) along the Athabasca River, north of Calling Lake. Recent clear-cuts (0-5 years old) are also shown. (Map: Forest Watch Alberta)

ence of open water (Timoney et al., 1997). The larger the watercourse, the more likely that this pattern will be observed. Another pattern clearly apparent at the regional scale is the preferential targeting of old-growth stands for harvesting (Fig. 8.4).

At the provincial scale, it is evident that relatively few townships within the boreal plain contain more than 25% old-growth of commercially-harvested species (Fig. 8.5). This is because old-growth in the boreal forest is widely distributed, and rarely clumped into specific regions, with the exception of large river valleys. This pattern also reflects the simple fact that almost a third of northern Alberta is comprised of non-merchantable peatlands and wetlands of various types (See Fig. 1.5).

In contrast to the boreal forest, the representation of commercially harvested old-growth in the East Slopes is relatively high throughout (Fig. 8.5). This is primarily because most townships there contain a high proportion of commercial forest (typically comprised of long-lived coniferous species) and few peatlands are present. Differences in drainage patterns, soil type, and climate, all contribute to the observed differences in forest composition (and hence old-growth) between the East Slopes and boreal regions. Whether there are also significant differences in the rate of fire between these two regions, contributing to observed differences in the occurrence of old-growth, is an open question. On one hand, the irregular topography of the foothills may limit the spread and ultimate size of fires, relative to the boreal plain. However, the deciduous and mixedwood stands typical of the boreal forest appear to have intrinsically lower probabilities of burning than the pure coniferous stands that dominate the foothills (Cumming, 2000).

Management of Old-Growth
Current Management

Forestry policy in Alberta continues to be fundamentally based on sustained-yield management (AEP, 1996). Sustained-yield means that forestry companies must ensure that their rate of harvest does not exceed the rate of tree growth; however, there are no requirements for maintaining old-growth on the landscape. In fact, the general practice, as reflected in the *Alberta Operating Ground Rules,* is to cut the oldest trees first (AEP, 1994a).

Because old-growth stands support the greatest diversity of forest species, the current policy of old-growth liquidation will have a significant detrimental impact on biodiversity (Stelfox, 1995: *viii*). Species with highly specialized habitat requirements restricting them to old-growth stands will be affected earliest and most severely. Studies on forest birds (Benkman, 1993; Schieck and Nietfeld, 1995), bats (Crampton and Barclay, 1998), insects (Niemela et al., 1993) and non-vascular plants (Crites and Dale, 1995) have all concluded that population declines of specialist species are likely to occur if old-growth is eliminated from the landscape. Other species that are found in multiple age classes but have their highest abundance in old-growth will also be affected. In some cases the impact will be large, because individuals currently observed in younger age classes will disappear once the core old-growth population, responsible for most reproduction, is eliminated.

Widespread declines in old-growth species have not yet been observed in Alberta, because substantial tracts of old-growth remain (though systematic surveys of rare species have never been conducted). However, Finnish and Scandinavian forests, where old-growth stands have been greatly

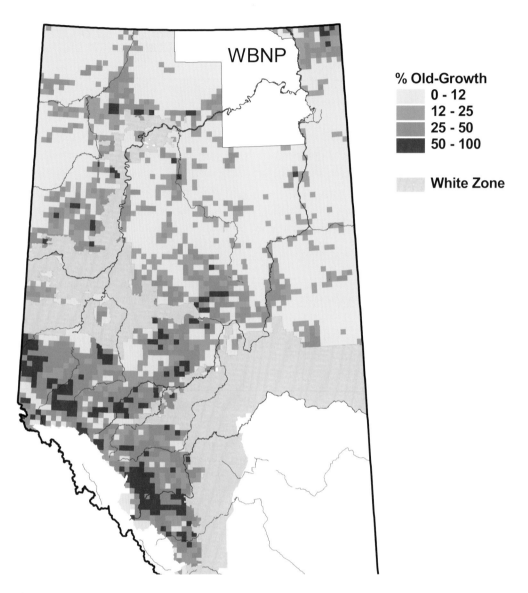

Fig. 8.5. Percentage of old-growth forest (> 100 years) per township. Forest types that are not commercially harvested are not included. Data from Alberta Phase 3 inventory, current to 2000.

reduced, provide evidence that concerns about old-growth species are well founded (Virkkala et al., 1994; Niemela, 1999). In Finland, several bird species that are old-growth specialists are in decline and their distribution is becoming concentrated in nature reserves, where substantial quantities of old-growth persist (Virkkala et al., 1994). Several species of insects that are now rare or extinct in Finland have been found in abundance immediately across the border in Russian Karelia, where old-growth has not been eliminated by harvesting operations (Siitonen and Martikainen, 1994). Overall, it is estimated that forestry operations in Fennoscandia have resulted in the decline of many hundreds of species (Niemela, 1999).

A Strategy for the Management of Old-Growth

Among biologists working on boreal systems there is a clear consensus that the retention of an appropriate amount of old-growth is necessary for the maintenance of forest biodiversity (Benkman, 1993; Bergeron et al., 1999; Burton et al., 1999; Niemela, 1999; Timoney, 2000). Studies commissioned by the Government of Alberta have also made recommendations to this effect:

> *Provincial government agencies and the forest industry are therefore encouraged to: . . . recognize the existence of a distinctive "old-growth" stage in aspen mixedwood forests and ensure that appropriate frequencies of older seral stages are maintained in the boreal forest landscape* (Stelfox, 1995: viii).

> *Maintaining current levels of forest-based biodiversity within the boreal forest natural region will require perpetuation of the full range of seral stages. There is no doubt that the most important and threatened age-class is old-growth* (AEP, 1998: 46).

The need to retain older age classes of forest is also specified in the Alberta Forest Conservation Strategy (AFCSSC, 1997: 10).

If old-growth is to be retained on the landscape with the objective of maintaining its associated biodiversity, then a comprehensive strategy for old-growth management is required. This strategy must include: (1) appropriate targets for the quantity of old-growth to be retained, (2) targets for the spatial distribution of old-growth, including the distribution of patch size, and (3) a dynamic planning framework designed to ensure that the targets will be achieved continuously (i.e., without periodic gaps). All targets must be defined by stand type.

Amount of Old-Growth to be Maintained

In general terms, the appropriate quantity of old-growth is defined by the Natural Disturbance Model (NDM) of forest harvesting. Under this model the target would be the amount of old-growth that occurs as a result of natural cycles of disturbance (fire) and forest regeneration. Although the NDM is conceptually straight-forward, it is difficult to apply in practice (see Chapter 7). Our estimates of the rate of burning and our understanding of forest regeneration are both inadequate for predicting the patterns of old-growth that would arise from any specific fire regime.

An alternative approach for defining old-growth targets is to utilize the patterns present in the existing forest. The Alberta Phase 3 inventory is the only data set providing provincial coverage, so it will have to be used for initial guidance (e.g., Fig. 8.2). It is best to use regional estimates because locally-derived estimates are usually biased by the impact of large historic fires (or lack thereof) (Cumming et al, 1996). However, systematic errors in the photo-interpretation of stand age and the cumulative impact of historical logging imply that the Phase 3 inventory underestimates the natural amount of old-growth, possibly by a large margin (Cumming et al., 2000; Timoney, 2001). On the other hand, fire suppression is likely to have had at least some effect, even if it is not as large as sometimes claimed (See Chapter 6). Further research will be required to determine whether these two biases cancel each other out, or whether adjustments to the initial old-growth targets are required.

Spatial Distribution of Old-Growth

The NDM can also be used to define targets for the spatial distribution of old-growth. As previously discussed, the basic pattern is generated by fire, but individual sites differ in their susceptibility to burning (Angelstam, 1998). It follows that harvesting should be concentrated where the probability of burning is highest, and sites that are unlikely to burn should be harvested at a very low rate (if at all). Scandinavian researchers have formalized this concept into the so-called ASIO model, which stands for Absent, Seldom, Infrequent, and Often (Angelstam, 1998). Under this model, sites are assigned an ASIO category on the basis of estimated fire frequency (using variables such as proximity to water, slope, aspect, etc.) and their rate of harvest is set accordingly.

Another aspect of spatial pattern that needs to be considered is patch size (where patches are contiguous stands of the same age class). Conventional harvesting practices produce cut-blocks of relatively fixed size, and the old-growth stands that will eventually arise from such practices will have minimal variability in size (Fig. 8.6). Of particular concern is the lack of production of large old-growth patches, as some species prefer the interior of stands away from the effects of exterior edges (Mladenoff et al., 1993; Paton, 1994). To avoid such problems, the targeted objective should be to maintain a natural distribution of patch sizes.

Operationally, the achievement of a natural patch-size distribution implies the introduction of variability into harvesting practices at multiple scales. Small patches of old-growth (i.e., < 2 ha) are typically most numerous and can best be generated by leaving clumps of live trees within harvested stands and by leaving small isolated stands unharvested. Variability of medium-sized patches (2-60 ha) can best be achieved by varying the size of harvest blocks (Fig. 8.6). Finally, the production of large patches of old-growth can be accomplished by designing the layout of harvest blocks such that over time large contiguous patches of old-growth are produced (Ohman and Eriksson, 1998). In some cases it would be desirable to aggregate logging at the township scale over a period of 20-30 years, to simulate the impact of a very large fire, and then remove all roads and leave the entire region untouched for 100 or more years.

Landscape-level Planning

The implementation of the old-growth management strategy described above is an extremely complex undertaking. To summarize, there are targets for the quantity of old-growth, by stand type, targets for the spatial distribution of old-growth, based on ASIO site factors, and targets for the distribution of old-growth patch size. These targets are to be maintained continuously, in the face of ongoing forest harvesting and wildfire, and in spite of initial age distributions that may be highly skewed in local management areas. Needless to say, implementation will have to occur in stages, as the required data and capacity for planning are acquired.

Initial priority should be given to retaining appropriate amounts of old-growth on the landscape. This can be achieved by allowing a portion of the older stands to escape harvest. Operationally, the objective is a tapered age distribution, as

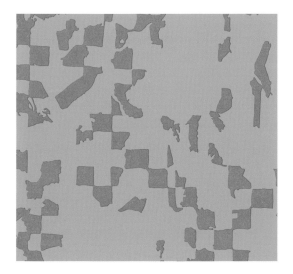

Fig. 8.6. Spatial pattern of harvest blocks. On the left are blocks cut within the past five years, demonstrating the conventional pattern. On the right is a pattern designed to maintain the natural distribution of old-growth patch sizes. The total area of harvest is approximately the same in both figures. (Map: Forest Watch Alberta)

described by Burton et al. (1999) (Fig. 8.7). The total amount of old-growth and age of the oldest stands would be based on provincial Phase 3 inventory data, by stand type, as previously described. The intent is to achieve these targets in perpetuity; however, it is recognized that skewness in the existing age structure in some forest management areas will result in transient deficiencies in some age classes at the regional level. This is not a concern as long as provincial targets are maintained. The expected impact of fire and other disturbances must be included in harvest plans so that the targeted distribution of old stands is actually achieved (Burton et al., 1999).

Targets for the spatial distribution of old-growth can best be achieved in the short-term through the establishment of old-growth reserves where no harvesting will occur over the next 20-year planning cycle. An obvious candidate for the core of this reserve is the existing system of ripar-

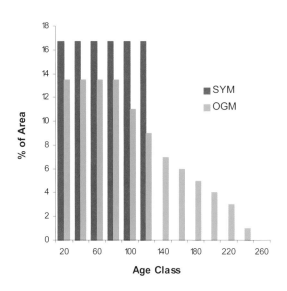

Fig. 8.7. A comparison of hypothetical target age structures under sustained-yield management (SYM) and old-growth management (OGM).

129

ian buffers (Cumming and Schmiegelow, 2001). The rate of burning in riparian areas is lower than in the surrounding uplands (fulfilling ASIO criteria) (Larsen, 1997) and they are able to serve as ready-made movement corridors, connecting old-growth patches throughout the landscape (Machtans et al., 1996). Because no harvesting is currently permitted in riparian buffer zones, there would be no impact on current harvest levels.

Any remaining large contiguous patches or local clusters of old-growth should also be incorporated into the reserve system. These large patches should account for a substantial portion of the total old-growth target area (Fairbarns, 1991; Niemela, 1999). Without special interim protection it is likely that remaining large patches of old-growth will be fragmented before a comprehensive system of dynamic planning is in place. Fragmentation by roads and seismic lines is a related issue that also needs to be addressed, likely by restricting new linear development in the reserve until it becomes part of the active land base again.

Large stands of old-growth white spruce, especially along major river valleys, should be given priority for protection because only a fraction of historic amounts of this stand type remain after decades of intensive harvesting (Timoney, 1996; AEP, 1998: 46). Furthermore, recent studies have demonstrated that the risk of fire in pure coniferous stands is substantially higher than in aspen-dominated mixedwoods (Cumming, 2000). Therefore, white spruce regeneration based on monoculture plantations may expose stands to excessive risk of fire (vs. mixedwood regeneration), and thereby fail to produce adequate amounts of old-growth.

The initial system of extended harvest ages and fixed old-growth reserves will achieve old-growth objectives in the short-term and keep options open for the future. However, fire will eventually fragment or completely obliterate most remaining large patches of old-growth (Johnson et al., 1998). Therefore, as soon as possible we need to implement a dynamic system of planning where new old-growth stands are continually produced to replace others that may be lost (especially the larger patches). Prototype computer models capable of such spatially-explicit harvest planning have been developed (e.g., Ohman and Eriksson, 1998; Baskent, 1999); however, they are not yet ready for commercial application. Additional data, including an ASIO classification of the landscape and better estimates of the amount and distribution of existing old-growth, are also required before such a system can be fully implemented.

Stand-level Management Issues

The old-growth management strategy, as part of a broader implementation of the NDM, should include a transition to mixedwood management wherever applicable. Mixedwood management involves the regeneration of white spruce through a natural mixedwood phase instead of current plantation management techniques that are designed to produce monocultures (Lieffers and Beck, 1994). Mixedwood stands are a prominent component of boreal old-growth and need to be maintained on the landscape (Stelfox, 1995: *viii*). With mixedwood management in place it will also be possible to define and achieve a more realistic target age structure for white spruce (e.g., Fig. 8.1), in place of the artificial age structure generated through monoculture regeneration (e.g., Fig. 8.7).

Another important component of old-growth management at the stand-level is the retention of live merchantable trees at the time of harvest. Larger clumps of such trees serve to maintain old-growth at the micro-scale, simulating the small unburned islands that typically remain after fire (Eberhart and Woodard, 1987). Residual live trees also provide at least some of the structural legacy that normally passes from the pre-fire stand to the new regenerating stand (Lee et al., 1997). The legacy of the pre-fire stand is responsible for much of the species diversity in young regenerating stands. It should not be construed, however, that leaving residual structure at the time of harvest reduces the need for old-growth (Schieck et al., 2000). As previously described, old-growth stands have the highest levels of species diversity, including many specialist species that are not found in other age classes (Niemela et al., 1993; Crites and Dale, 1995; Kirk et al., 1996). Furthermore, most species that are found in both young and old stands have their highest abundance in old-growth stands (Stelfox, 1995: *vii*; Schieck et al., 2000). It is questionable whether these species would persist if core breeding populations in old-growth stands were eliminated (Schieck et al., 2000).

Literature Cited

AEP (Alberta Environmental Protection). 1994a. Timber harvest planning and ground rules. Alberta Environmental Protection, Edmonton, AB. (Available at: www.gov.ab.ca/env/forests.html)

AEP (Alberta Environmental Protection). 1994b. Natural Regions of Alberta. Alberta Environmental Protection, Edmonton, AB.

AEP (Alberta Environmental Protection). 1996. The status of Alberta's timber supply. (Available at: www.gov.ab.ca/env/forests.html)

AEP (Alberta Environmental Protection). 1998. The Boreal Forest Natural Region of Alberta. Alberta Environmental Protection, Edmonton, AB.

AFCSSC (Alberta Forest Conservation Strategy Steering Committee). 1997. Alberta forest conservation strategy. Alberta Environmental Protection, Edmonton, AB. (Available at: www.borealcentre.ca/reports/reports.html).

ASRD (Alberta Sustainable Resource Development). 2002. Provincial fire database. (Available at: www.gov.ab.ca/env/forests.html)

Angelstam, P. K. 1998. Maintaining and restoring biodiversity in European boreal forests by developing natural disturbance regimes. J. Veg. Sci. 9:593-602.

Anonymous. 1985. Alberta phase 3 inventory: an overview. ENR report I/86. Alberta Forest Service, Edmonton, AB.

Baskent, E. 1999. Controlling spatial structure of forested landscapes: a case study towards landscape management. Land. Ecol. 14:83-97.

Benkman, C. 1993. Logging, conifers, and the conservation of crossbills. Cons. Biol. 7:473-479.

Bergeron, Y., B. Harvey, A. Leduc, and S. Gauthier. 1999. Forest management guidelines based on natural disturbance dynamics: stand and forest-level considerations. For. Chron. 75:49-54.

Burton, P., D. Kneeshaw, and D. Coates. 1999. Managing forest harvesting to maintain old growth in boreal and sub-boreal forests. For. Chron. 75:623-631.

Crampton, L.H. and R.M. Barclay. 1998. Selection of roosting and foraging habitat by bats in different-aged aspen mixedwood stands. Cons. Ecol. 12: 1347-1358.

Crites, S. and M. Dale. 1995. Relationships between non-vascular species and stand age and stand structure in aspen mixedwood forests in Alberta. Pages 91-114 in Stelfox, B., editor. Relationships Between Stand Age, Stand Structure, and Biodiversity in Aspen Mixedwood Forests in Alberta. Alberta Environmental Centre, Vegreville, AB. (Available at: www.borealcentre.ca/reports/reports.html)

Cumming, S. 2000. Forest type, fire ignition, and fire frequency in boreal mixedwood forests. SFM Working Paper WP 2000-11. (Available at: http://sfm-1.biology.ualberta.ca/english/home/index.htm)

Cumming, S. 2001. Forest type and wildfire in the Alberta boreal mixedwood: what do fires burn? Ecol. Appl. 11: 97-110.

Cumming, S., P. Burton, and B. Klinkenberg. 1996. Boreal mixedwood forests may have no "representative" regions: some implications for reserve design. Ecography 19:162-180.

Cumming, S., F. Schmiegelow, and P. Burton. 2000. Gap dynamics in boreal aspen stands: is the forest older than we think? Ecol. Appl. 10:744-759.

Cumming, S., and F. Schmiegelow. 2001. Effects of habitat abundance and configuration, and the forest matrix, on distributional patterns of boreal birds. SFM Working Paper WP 2001-1. (Available at: http://sfm-1.biology.ualberta.ca/english/home/index.htm)

Eberhart, K. and P. Woodard. 1987. Distribution of residual vegetation associated with large fires in Alberta. Can. J. For. Res. 17:1207-1212.

Esseen, P., K. Renhorn, and R. Peettersson. 1996. Epiphytic lichen biomass in managed and old-growth boreal forests: effect of branch quality. Ecol. Appl. 6:228-238.

Fairbarns, M. 1991. Old growth in the boreal mixedwood forest section. Alberta Forestry, Lands, and Wildlife, Edmonton, AB.

Forest Watch Alberta. 2001. Planning and practices survey of Forest Management Agreement holders in Alberta. Forest Watch Alberta, Edmonton, AB. (Available at: www.forestwatchalberta.ca)

Greene, D., J. Zasada, L. Sirois, D. Kneeshaw, H. Morin, I. Charron, and M. Simard. 1999. A review of the regeneration dynamics of North American boreal forest tree species. Can. J. For. Res. 29:824-839.

Johnson, E. and C. Van Wagner. 1985. The theory and use of two fire history models. Can. J. For. Res. 15:214-220.

Johnson, E. A., K. Miyanishi, and J. M. H. Weir. 1998. Wildfires in the western Canadian boreal forest: landscape patterns and ecosystem management. J. Veg. Sci. 9:603-610.

Kirk, D., A. Diamond, K. Hobson, and A. Smith. 1996. Breeding bird communities of the western and northern Canadian boreal forest: relationship to forest type. Can. J. of Zool. 74:1749-1770.

Kneeshaw, D. and Y. Bergeron. 1998. Canopy gap characteristics and tree replacement in the southeastern boreal forest. Ecology 79:783-794.

Larsen, C. 1997. Spatial and temporal variations in boreal fire frequency in northern Alberta. J. Biogeog. 24:663-673.

Lee, P., S. Hanus, and B. Grover. 2000. Criteria for estimating old growth in boreal mixedwoods from standard timber inventory data. For. Ecol. Manage. 129:25-30.

Lee, P. C., S. Crites, M. Nietfeld, H. V. Nguyen, and J. B. Stelfox. 1997. Characteristics and origins of deadwood material in aspen-dominated boreal forests. Ecol. Applic. 7:691-701.

Lieffers, V. and J. Beck. 1994. A semi-natural approach to mixedwood management in the prairie provinces. For. Chron. 70:260-264.

Lieffers, V., R. Macmillan, D. MacPherson, K. Branter, and J. Stewart. 1996. Semi-natural and intensive silvicultural systems for the boreal mixedwood forest. For. Chron. 72:286-292.

Machtans, C., M. Villard, and S. Hannon. 1996. Use of riparian buffer strips as movement corridors by forest birds. Cons. Biol. 10:1366-1379.

Martikainen, P., J. Siitonen, P. Punttila, L. Kaila, and J. Rauh. 1999. Species richness of Coleoptera in mature managed and old-growth boreal forests in southern Finland. For. Ecol. Manage. 116:233-245.

McClelland, B. and P. McClelland. 1999. Pileated woodpecker nest and roost trees in Montana: links with old-growth and forest "health". Wildl. Soc. Bull. 27:846-857.

Mladenoff, D. J., M. A. White, J. Pastor, and T. R. Crow. 1993. Comparing spatial pattern in unaltered old-growth and disturbed old forest landscapes. Ecol. Appl. 3:294-306.

Niemela, J. 1999. Management in relation to disturbance in the boreal forest. For. Ecol. Manage. 115:127-134.

Ohman, K. and L. Eriksson. 1998. The core area concept in forming contiguous areas for long-term forest planning. Can. J. For. Res. 28:1032-1039.

Paton, P. 1994. The effect of edge on avian nest success: how strong is the evidence? Cons. Biol. 8:17-26.

Roy, L., B. Stelfox, and J. Nolan. 1995. Relationships between mammal biodiversity and stand age and structure in aspen mixedwood forests in Alberta. Pages 159-189 in Stelfox, B., editor. Relationships between stand age, stand structure, and biodiversity in aspen mixedwood Forests in Alberta. Alberta Environmental Centre, Vegreville, AB. (Available at: www.borealcentre.ca/reports/reports.html).

Schieck, J. and M. Nietfeld. 1995. Bird species richness and abundance in relation to stand age and structure in aspen mixedwood forests in Alberta. Pages 115-157 in Stelfox, B., editor. Relationships between stand age, stand structure, and biodiversity in aspen mixedwood Forests in Alberta. Alberta Environmental Centre, Vegreville, AB. (Available at: www.borealcentre.ca/reports/reports.html).

Schieck, J., K. Stuart-Smith, and M. Norton. 2000. Bird communities are affected by amount and dispersion of vegetation retained in mixedwood boreal forest harvest areas. For. Ecol. Manage. 126:239-254.

Siitonen, J. and P. Martikainen. 1994. Occurrence of rare and threatened insects living on decaying *Populus tremula*: a comparison between Finnish and Russian Karelia. Scand. J. of For. Res. 9:185-191.

Stelfox, J. B. 1995. Relationships between stand age, stand structure, and biodiversity in aspen mixedwood Forests in Alberta. Alberta Environmental Centre, Vegreville, AB.

(Available at: www.borealcentre.ca/reports/reports.html)

Timoney, K. 1996. The logging of a world heritage site: Wood Buffalo National Park. For. Chron. 72:485-490.

Timoney, K. 2000. Old-growth forests in space and time: fire, logging, falsehoods, and old-growth conservation. Ecoforestry 15:7-16.

Timoney, K. 2001. Types and attributes of old-growth forests in Alberta, Canada. Nat. Areas J. 21:282-300.

Timoney, K., G. Peterson, and R. Wein. 1997. Vegetation development of boreal riparian communities after flooding, fire, and logging, Peace River, Canada. For. Ecol. Manage. 93:101-120.

Virkkala, R., A. Rajasarkka, R. A. Vaisanen, M. Vickholm, and E. Virolainen. 1994. The significance of protected areas for the land birds of southern Finland. Cons. Biol. 8:532-544.

R. Schneider

9. Putting it all Together

The Alberta Forest Conservation Strategy (AFCS), representing several years of deliberation among a full spectrum of forest stakeholders, provides the foundation for a new approach to forest management in Alberta (AFCSSC, 1997:1):

> *The Alberta Forest Conservation Strategy calls for significant change in how activities are planned and carried out in forest ecosystems at the legislative, commercial and personal level. The change has to do with giving forest ecosystems first consideration in all that we do, to ensure that the forest and forested lands of Alberta will continue to provide a sustainable flow of goods and services for many generations to come.*

According to the AFCS the implementation of this new system of forest management is to be based on the paradigm of Ecological Forest Management (EFM) (AFCSSC, 1997:11). In the previous three chapters I have reviewed the basic concepts of EFM, as described in the scientific literature. Here I pull the pieces together to illustrate what a workable system might look like in Alberta.

Integrated Management Plans

The objectives of the AFCS cannot be achieved without long-term integrated planning. This entails developing a comprehensive integrated management plan that governs resource allocation, coordinates the activities of all operators on the landscape, and guides regulatory decision-making. Regional differences in land use patterns and forest characteristics dictate that a set of regional plans will be required, not just a single plan. The number of regional management plans for northern Alberta should be limited to four or five to ensure that planning areas are large enough to achieve large-scale ecological objectives.

The plans should not be overly prescriptive, but instead should focus on defining a set of measurable ecological and socio-economic objectives that are relevant across a long planning horizon (e.g., 100 years). Together, these objectives should effectively define a desired future forest that is consistent with the AFCS and bounded by realistic expectations of what can actually be achieved (AFMSC, 1997: 4).

Benefits of Regional Planning

A shift to fully integrated forest-based planning is a prerequisite for managing cumulative impacts and maintaining the ecological integrity of the forest. But regional planning has many additional benefits that make it highly desirable. These benefits include:

1. **Cost savings.** Cumming and Armstrong (1999) have shown that major savings in the cost of hauling timber and constructing roads could be achieved through a system of regional harvest planning. Harmonizing the construction of roads among industrial sectors would result in additional savings. It is also simpler and more cost effective to develop a single harvest plan for a region than it is to develop several overlapping plans independently.

2. **Reduced inter-sectoral conflicts.** The number of operators from different industrial sectors is now so high that land use conflicts have become commonplace (Ross, 2001). Regional planning provides a way of dealing with these problems proactively and systematically.

3. **Increased productivity.** A transition to regional management would enable the widespread implementation of mixedwood management. By harnessing natural processes instead of working against them, this approach increases the overall productivity of the forest relative to monoculture plantations (Lieffers et al., 1996).

4. **Stable softwood harvest.** Under the existing management regime the current volume of softwood harvest cannot be sustained (see Chapter 5). Cumming and Armstrong (1999) demonstrated that regional harvest planning could alleviate the looming shortage of softwood timber by making better use of the available wood. Regional management that incorporates floating old-growth reserves would also maintain the supply of large logs required by mills that produce dimensional lumber.

5. **Effective monitoring and reporting.** The current jumble of forest management plans and limited requirements for compliance monitoring make it exceedingly difficult for the public to ascertain how well forestry companies are managing the forest. The impacts of the petroleum sector are even harder to assess, given that literally hun-

dreds of companies are operative in any given region and there is no comprehensive system for tracking their activities. The adoption of a regional approach to management would greatly facilitate monitoring and regular reporting to the public on the overall state of the forest.

6. **Protected areas.** Under the current system forestry companies with cutting rights in a proposed protected area bear the brunt of the lost harvest volume, while others are unaffected. Regional planning, involving reform of the tenure system, removes this barrier to the establishment of new protected areas by distributing any reduction in harvest volume among all companies. Protected areas can, therefore, be located where they are most needed to fulfill their role as representative benchmarks, not relegated to areas that are otherwise undesirable.

7. **Access to markets.** Regional management plans designed to maintain ecological integrity of the forest should meet the environmental criteria for the highest standards of forest certification. Therefore, all companies operating under the regional plan should be certifiable and thereby maintain their access to markets in the future.

Plan Development

The primary role of the regional planning process is to define clear and measurable management objectives that will achieve the vision and goal of the AFCS. This entails finding a balance between ecological and economic objectives, in the context of the desired future forest.

The first step is to assign all responsibility for regional planning to a single government agency. The plans developed by this agency must constrain and guide decision-making by other government agencies that handle the mechanics of project approvals and operational planning. This implies a shift to hierarchical decision-making, which would entail significant organizational restructuring within government. The Division of Integrated Resource Management could fulfill the role of regional planner; however, it currently lacks the resources and political backing required to do so. The extent to which additional support is provided to this Division in the future will serve as a measure of the government's commitment to the reform of forest management.

The entire planning process must be bounded by the finite ability of the forest to meet the demands placed on it, as not all desired futures are possible (AFMSC, 1997: 4). To do this the plan must demonstrate that a workable management approach exists for achieving all of the objectives. This latter requirement enormously complicates matters because there is no direct way to work backward from the desired outcome to the process of getting there. Instead, management regimes must be developed and assessed in a process of iterative refinement.

The process of exploring and assessing alternative management regimes is facilitated by computer models serving as decision-support tools. Given the inherent complexity of forest ecosystems and human land uses, these models must in fact be considered a necessity. The tools that are currently available include *ALCES* (see Chapter 5) and *TARDIS* (Cumming and Armstrong, 1999), both of which were developed in Alberta. These models project the state of the forest into the future under alternative management regimes, providing a variety of ecological and economic measures as output.

In practice, development of regional plans will likely require an iterative process, facilitated and led by the Division of Integrated Resource Management (with scientific and technical support). The government's role would be to lead stakeholders through a process of defining alternative management scenarios and assessing their relative merits in the context of the desired future forest (AFMSC, 1997: 4). The basic elements of such a process have been incorporated into a pilot project involving the northern East Slopes (AE, 2002). Because the pilot is still underway as of this writing it is too soon to determine how well it will achieve the objectives I have outlined here.

Because the development of management plans will likely involve regional stakeholder groups, the potential exists for local economic interests to be overrepresented. Local economic interests may be directly impacted by the management plan; therefore, it is certainly appropriate that their input is included in the process. However, economic objectives cannot be permitted to override the ecological objectives expressed in the AFCS. If insufficient input regarding ecological objectives is provided through a regional stakeholder process, then steps must be taken to obtain it through alternative means. One solution is to establish a provincial advisory board charged with ensuring that ecological objectives are adequately and consistently incorporated into the regional plans. Ultimately, it is the duty of the government, as manager and primary steward of the forest on behalf of the public owners, to make management decisions that reflect the broad public interest.

In its final form each regional management plan must provide a set of well-defined and measurable management objectives applicable to the entire planning region. The following is a list of the key elements that should be included:

1. **Zonation.** The plan needs to define the boundaries of protected areas within the planning region. Selection of sites should follow the design principles described in Chapter 7. The location of areas where intensive forest management is permitted, if any, also needs to be defined. All remaining forest should be managed according to the principles of EFM.

2. **Ecological objectives.** The ultimate ecological objective, as specified in the AFCS, is the maintenance of the ecological integrity of the forest, including the maintenance of biodiversity. However, this objective is difficult to apply in practice. Therefore, the management plan needs to include a series of sub-objectives that collectively ensure that critical ecological processes and the habitat needs of most species are maintained. Examples of these "coarse filter" objectives include the proportion of forest to be retained in the old-growth stage, the maximum density of roads and other linear features, and targets related to the emulation of natural disturbances (see Chapters 6 and 8 for more detail). Additional "fine filter" objectives will need to be specified for species that have unique habitat requirements or are at risk of extinction.

3. **Socio-economic objectives.** The management plan should define the maximum volume of timber harvest consistent with the maintenance of ecological integrity (as determined through modelling exercises). Given that sustained-yield management has maximized harvest rates at the expense of long-term ecological objectives, a rebalanc-

ing of objectives under the new system implies a reduction in the rate of harvest. Socio-economic objectives should also include measures of long-term sustainability of economic benefits, and cultural benefits that cannot be defined in economic terms (e.g., traditional land-use practices).

Implementation — Forestry Sector

A major overhaul of harvest planning will be required to implement the regional management plans as described. The current hodgepodge system divides responsibility for harvest planning among multiple overlapping tenure holders and the government, making it all but impossible to achieve regional ecological objectives. For example, maintaining large-scale spatial patterns through aggregated harvest or implementing a system of floating old-growth reserves cannot be accomplished under the current system.

The solution is to place all responsibility for harvest planning back with the Land and Forest Service (under the direction of the Division of Integrated Resource Management), reversing the recent trend towards devolution of management responsibility. I make this recommendation with some trepidation because it has been industry, not government, that has shown leadership in implementing EFM over the past several years. However, from a longer-term perspective government control of the process is a necessity. The problem is that only a few forestry companies have demonstrated meaningful progress. Furthermore, companies that have embraced EFM, such as Al-Pac and Daishowa-Marubeni, may be sold tomorrow. In fact, this is exactly what has happened to Daishowa's northern operations, which are now reverting back to sustained-yield management under Tolko. There is also a serious problem in

accountability. Expecting forestry companies that are in the business of cutting down trees to maintain the ecological integrity of forests as their top priority presents too great a conflict of interest. Finally, too many factors affecting the forest are beyond the ability of forestry companies to control.

The Land and Forest Service currently does not have the staff or resources required for the complex and technically intensive process of long-term harvest planning. Consequently, the Service has to be substantially expanded or, alternatively, the technical aspects of planning have to be contracted out. Either option is workable. Organizations that currently have the capacity to undertake harvest planning at the regional scale include forest management companies such as Timberline and the planning departments of larger FMA holders. To maintain stability and continuity, outsourcing would have to be done on the basis of exclusive long-term contracts (e.g., five years). To maintain innovation and efficiency the renewal of contracts should be opened to tender.

The final step required for implementing the regional plans is a reallocation of the timber supply. Current allocations, based on sustained-yield management, need to be aligned with the harvest volume defined in the regional management plans. In addition, area-based Forest Management Agreements need to be converted to volume-based tenure agreements to facilitate zonal planning and the implementation of aggregated harvest protocols (see below). The reallocation of timber supply could be done by direct government assignment, as has been done in the past. Alternatively, it could be accomplished through a free-market system whereby companies bid for long-term (e.g., 20-year) volume rights. A benefit of the free-market approach is that it may help resolve the softwood lumber dispute with the United States. During a transition phase of perhaps five years, current harvest volumes of all existing forestry companies would be maintained. After the phase-in period the total harvest volume would be limited to the maximum rate defined in the regional management plan.

Implementation — Petroleum Sector

Although the petroleum industry cuts almost the same area of forest as the forestry industry, the two sectors are fundamentally different. Trees are the commodity on which the forest industry is based, whereas for the petroleum sector trees are just something that gets in the way. The lack of a vested interest in the forest explains why the petroleum sector has never engaged in reforestation or landscape planning (though one wonders why the government has never compelled it to do so). As a result, the gulf between the current system of management and EFM is much wider for the petroleum sector than for the forestry sector. On the positive side, there is no intrinsic reason for the petroleum sector to oppose a reduction in rate of cutting, as long as access to underground reserves remains possible.

Ideally, regional harvest plans developed for the forestry sector should be fully integrated with long-term operational plans that define the spatial layout and timing of future petroleum developments. This approach would minimize the additive impact of the two sectors. Unfortunately, the petroleum sector in Alberta is not at all amenable to centralized operational planning. Whereas there are only 11 companies with area-based tenures in the forestry sector, there are several hundred companies with area-based tenures in the petroleum sector. Moreover, subsurface mineral leases are typically only a few hundred ha in size; therefore, regional management plans would impinge upon literally thousands of existing leases worth hundreds of millions of dollars. An even more fundamental problem is that finding and developing underground petroleum reserves involves a fair degree of chance. Therefore, it is not possible for a centralized operating plan to assign a specific volume of oil to a petroleum company in the same way that a specific volume of wood can be assigned to a forestry company. Finally, the pace of activity in the petroleum sector is influenced primarily by economic factors, which introduces substantial variability into the timing of petroleum developments.

If centralized operational planning of the petroleum industry is not possible, then integration of activities must occur at the level of the regional management plan. This could be accomplished by setting limits on the amount of cumulative disturbance, using such measures as total area in a non-forest state and density of linear features. Under this system petroleum companies would retain their existing subsurface tenure rights, but the right to disturb the forest would be subject to a competitive bidding process. The cost of these disturbance rights would provide an incentive for petroleum companies to implement practices that minimize the amount of disturbance. Restoration would be another option, and in fact would be a requirement in areas where the disturbance threshold had already been reached.

If the right to conduct surface disturbance became a tradable commodity, then the future of the forest industry might come into question. This is because the petroleum sector, generating 100 times the revenue of the forestry sector, may find it expedient to simply buy out forestry companies to garner their disturbance rights. If such a scenario was not felt to be in the public interest then the regional plan could reserve a fixed proportion of the disturbance allocation for the forest industry. The petroleum industry would have to work with what is left.

Legislative Reform

The Division of Integrated Resource Management has initiated a process of regional planning that could realize the changes in forest management I have described. But experience with similar initiatives in the past suggests that success will not be forthcoming unless changes in policy are supported by changes in legislation. In his review of the current Integrated Resource Management initiative, Kennett (2002) drew the following conclusions:

> *The reliance on policy instruments without detailed legal underpinnings would have three implications for regional strategies. First, interested parties would not be able to rely on specific legal requirements in the event that the proposed process for developing and implementing regional strategies is not completed, or the manner in which it is carried out is contested. Second, regional strategies as integrative mechanisms would be subordinate to other legal mandates and requirements that may not fully reflect principles of Integrated Resource Management. There would be no legal accountability mechanism should decision makers fail to comply with them. Finally, the failure to entrench the regional strategy process and its products in legislation would increase their vulnerability to shifts in political direction and funding priorities, such as those that undercut the [earlier] Integrated Resource Plan process.*

It seems clear that reform of forest management must be accompanied by legislative reform. In fact, the AFCS includes a formal recommendation to this effect (AFCSSC, 1997: 6). Given that most legislation pertaining to forest management dates back to the 1950s, such reform is long overdue. The updated *Forests Act* should enshrine the concept of EFM and the key elements of the AFCS as the basis for forest management in Alberta. In addition, the statutory basis for land-use planning needs to be streamlined and should provide the mandate and procedural requirements for developing integrated regional plans and controlling cumulative industrial impacts.

Lessons from Ontario

The notion that reforms as described here might actually be implemented may, to some, seem far-fetched. In fact, reforms of a similar nature and magnitude have already been realized in British Columbia, Ontario, and the Pacific Northwest of the United States.

The changes in forest management that have taken place in Ontario over the last decade are particularly illustrative of what might be accomplished in Alberta, given that both provinces share vast expanses of boreal forest and a Conservative government. Reforms in Ontario began with a class environmental assessment of Ontario's system of forest management, lasting from 1987 until 1992 (Euler and Epp, 2000: 278). The outcome of this assessment was a set of recommendations that share a remarkable similarity to the recommendations of the AFCS. Notably, both processes recommend that sustained-yield management be superseded by EFM (Euler and Epp, 2000: 280).

The major difference between the two review processes is that in Ontario the recommendations were actually implemented. To start, the concept of placing the integrity of the forest first was enshrined in the *Crown Forest Sustainability Act* (GOO, 1994: sec. 1):

> *The purposes of this Act are to provide for the sustainability of Crown forests and, in accordance with that objective, to manage Crown forests to meet social, economic and environmental needs of present and future generations. In this Act, "sustainability" means long term Crown forest health.*

The *Act* also defines two principles by which sustainability is to be determined (GOO, 1994: sec. 3):

> *1. Large, healthy, diverse and productive Crown forests and their associated ecological processes and biological diversity should be conserved.*
>
> *2. The long term health and vigour of Crown forests should be provided for by using forest practices that, within the limits of silvicultural requirements, emulate natural disturbances and landscape patterns while minimizing adverse effects on plant life, animal life, water, soil, air and social and economic values, including recreational values and heritage values.*

In addition to defining the general objectives of forest management the *Crown Forest Sustainability Act* also establishes requirements for planning. In particular, managers must prepare an explicit analysis of how forest management will affect the landscape, including measures of diversity (Euler and Epp, 2000: 286). There are also requirements pertaining to adaptive management and public input.

The reform of forest management in Ontario also included a process for establishing additional protected areas in the commercial forest zone. Through this process 378 new parks totaling 24,000 km^2 were established in 1999 (OFAAB, 2001). Discussions concerning the designation of additional areas are currently underway.

The Natural Disturbance Model

Under EFM, harvest planning and operational practices are to be based on the emulation of natural disturbances. Operating guidelines for implementing this approach at the stand-level are now becoming available in the scientific literature (e.g., Song, 2002; see Chapter 6). An important unresolved issue is how to adequately emulate the structural legacy left after fire in the form of standing dead trees and fire skips. Leaving clumps of live trees on cutblocks and limiting the salvage logging of fire-killed trees are both useful approaches. The question is, how much is enough?

In this instance ecological and economic objectives are diametrically opposed; therefore, the issue is not only a scientific one. Stakeholders need to evaluate the inherent tradeoffs through the exploration of alternative management scenarios and the final decision needs to reflect the broad public interest. Researchers should structure their studies and present their results in a way that facilitates this process. Studies that demonstrate the change in ecological response across multiple levels of a management intervention are of particular value. Once the decisions have been made they should be incorporated in an updated version of the provincial *Operating Ground Rules*.

At the landscape-scale the emulation of natural disturbances involves the application of harvest planning protocols that maintain landscape patterns similar to those produced by fire and natural regeneration (see Chapter 6). The pre-industrial forest provides the appropriate target landscape, when characterized at the scale of the regional management plans. Other approaches for defining the target landscape are theoretically possible, but are impractical to implement.

The full benefit of the natural disturbance approach can be realized only if it includes the emulation of very large fires, because these fires have the greatest ecological effect and account for most of the cumulative area burned. Emulating large fires requires that most forest harvesting be concentrated in a small number of sites. The size of these aggregated harvest areas would likely be in the range of 1-3 townships (100-300 km^2). Harvesting would take place over a relatively short period (e.g., 10-20 years), resulting in a reasonable approximation of a large even-aged patch. Further emulation of fire patterns could be achieved by leaving some stands unharvested, to represent fire skips, and by leaving residual structure within cutblocks, as previously described. Recent research by the Alberta Research Council recommends that up to 30% of merchantable trees should be retained in cutblock residuals, unharvested stands, and riparian buffers (Schieck and Song, 2002).

Intensive regeneration techniques, such as ground scarification, genetically selected stock, and herbicides, should not be used except on sites where natural regeneration is likely to fail and in intensive management zones defined in the regional plan. In mixedwood forests great care must be taken to preserve understory spruce and clumps of seed trees at the time of harvest because these trees are vital to the regeneration of softwoods under a low intervention approach. After

harvesting has been completed all roads would be reclaimed and the site left undisturbed for an extended period (e.g., 100 years).

To many in the conservation community the thought of implementing large harvest blocks is anathema. But this approach is actually far superior to the existing system of dispersed harvest for maintaining ecological integrity of the forest. The main reason is that the dispersed system of harvest requires the construction and maintenance of an extensive road network to provide continual accessibility to the entire management area. The existence of a permanent road network that permeates the forest to such a degree presents an unacceptable risk to the integrity of the forest. Secondly, aggregated harvest is necessary for achieving large-scale landscape patterns similar to those produced by fire. Maintaining large patches of old-growth could be accomplished by delaying the subsequent harvest of selected harvest sites for an extended period (i.e., floating old-growth reserves). Finally, by concentrating the harvest in a few areas, the majority of the management area would remain undisturbed. This is particularly significant when one considers that many management techniques designed to speed the regeneration of conifers involve multiple entries to the stand. It also means that only a small part of the forest will be exposed to early management trials, which carry the greatest uncertainty and highest risk of failure.

If the total area of harvest is held constant, then the implementation of an aggregated system of harvest will likely result in a reduction in harvest volume. This is because stands are selected for harvest on the basis of location, not volume, which is opposite to the current system. Moreover, many of the high-volume stands that might have been immediately harvested will lose volume due to aging before they are eventually scheduled for harvest. Older stands may also face a higher risk of fire. Finally, the removal of roads after harvest precludes the use of multiple-entry management techniques designed to maximize the rate of regeneration of conifers. This includes some of the techniques that have been proposed for mixedwood management. A further reduction in harvest volume will likely result from the implementation of measures to maintain old-growth.

Because implementing the natural disturbance approach at the landscape-scale is likely to result in a reduction in harvest volume it is again necessary to weigh tradeoffs between ecological and economic objectives. The evaluation is particularly challenging in this instance because many interacting variables need to be considered. For example, the number and size of aggregated harvest sites and the duration of harvest are all open to adjustment. Similarly, the number of old-growth reserves, their total area, and duration of existence are open variables. Cost savings through reduced road maintenance (which are likely to be considerable) and the additional cost of rebuilding roads after being reclaimed also need to be considered, along with the impact of wildfire. The "best" combination of variables will be that which stakeholders feel presents the correct balance between ecological and economic objectives, within the bounds of the AFCS. Making this decision will require an iterative approach involving computer models, as described in the section on regional plan development.

To this point I have avoided mention of the petroleum industry in the context of the natural disturbance model. This is because there is no natural disturbance analogue for most petroleum activities and because it is very difficult to in-corporate petroleum activities into long-term plans. One solution is to locate aggregated harvest sites in areas that have the highest potential for petroleum development. But this is only a partial solution because few harvest sites will be active at any time. In parts of the management area where the forest industry is not active disturbances by the petroleum industry should be reduced to the point that their ecological effects are negligible. Such "best" practices are already being implemented in areas of native prairie (Sinton, 2001). Similar practices applicable to forested areas have been developed, but are not yet in widespread use. Some examples of "best" practices include:

- minimizing road infrastructure by using existing roads or temporary winter access as much as possible, coordinating the construction of new roads with other industrial users, and removing well site access roads after drilling has been completed;
- minimizing cumulative linear disturbance by maximizing the spatial overlap of roads, seismic lines, pipelines, and power lines;
- limiting the width of seismic lines to 1.0 m on average and reforesting lines immediately after use;
- utilizing a meandering course when cutting seismic lines as well as intermittent blockage to preclude a linear corridor effect;
- well sites limited to 0.25 ha in size or less and multiple wells drilled from common pad;
- well sites immediately reforested after decommissioning;
- use of alternatives to fresh water for enhanced oil recovery; and
- reduction in flaring, spreading of oil wastes, and other forms of pollution.

Implementing even this preliminary list of best practices would be of enormous benefit in managing cumulative industrial impacts. To demonstrate this I incorporated a set of best practices into a new run of the *ALCES* simulation from Chapter 5 (Fig. 9.1). Using *ALCES* in this way also illustrates how models can be used to evaluate alternative management scenarios (though in practice additional output measures would be requested).

Adaptive Management and Protected Areas

The approach to planning presented in the previous sections presumes that the information required to make informed decisions is available. In reality, there are many gaps in our knowledge.

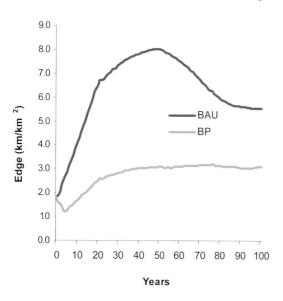

Fig. 9.1. Total density of linear disturbance edge in the Al-Pac FMA, predicted by ALCES simulation. BAU = Business as usual (see Chapter 5). BP = Best practices: 50% overlap in linear features; 50% road harmonization; seismic lines = 1.0 m and immediately reforested.

These gaps are most evident with respect to our understanding of ecological responses to human disturbances, especially at larger spatial scales and over longer periods of time. This is largely because large-scale long-term studies are difficult and costly to plan and implement and because natural systems are tremendously complex.

Because our knowledge base is incomplete it is important that decision-making be conducted in the context of the adaptive management approach, together with a healthy dose of the precautionary principle. Under adaptive management, management scenarios are treated as hypotheses, not fixed expectations (Walters, 1997). Careful monitoring is conducted to determine whether the system is in fact responding as expected. If not, adjustments are made to assumptions, models, and management practices in an effort to rectify the observed deviations. By implication, regional management plans and long-term harvest plans must be considered living documents that require continual updating and revision.

Two types of monitoring are required to support the adaptive management process. The first is compliance monitoring, designed to verify that the management plan is being carried out as planned and that operational targets are being achieved. The second is biodiversity monitoring, designed to evaluate whether the plan is fulfilling its ultimate mandate of maintaining biodiversity in the face of industrial activity. The provincial biodiversity monitoring program (www.fmf.ab.ca/bm.html), now in the pilot phase, is ideally suited for meeting the biodiversity monitoring needs of adaptive management. This program should be implemented as soon as possible.

In addition to the *reactive* use of adaptive management, as described above, this approach can and should be used in a *proactive* manner (also known as passive vs. active adaptive management). With proactive adaptive management an effort is made to identify key uncertainties inherent in the management scenarios while they are being developed. Experimental management trials are then implemented on the landscape in an effort to resolve these key uncertainties, leading to more robust predictions and better management decisions.

Our limited understanding of natural systems and the inherent limitations of the natural disturbance model dictate that an expanded system of protected areas be established to help manage the risk of species loss on the industrial landscape. Protected areas also function as ecological benchmarks, providing appropriate control sites for monitoring under adaptive management and sites for future research into natural systems. Design criteria for selecting new protected areas and the optimal location for a set of new large areas designed to fill existing gaps in ecosystem representation were described in Chapter 7.

Economic Realities

Forestry Sector

The factor most responsible for impeding the implementation of EFM is concern over diminished economic returns. Within the forestry sector, new requirements for maintaining old-growth, leaving residual live trees in cutblocks, establishing new protected areas, and implementing an aggregated harvest system will collectively reduce the volume of timber harvest from current levels. Some of the loss in timber flow will be offset by gains in efficiency and productivity under the new system (Cumming and Armstrong, 1999), but not all of it.

Scientific research and computer-based decision-support tools will help clarify and quantify the exact nature of trade-offs between ecological and economic objectives. However, the final decision is not a scientific one — it ultimately hinges on societal values (given that the forests in question are publicly owned). In this context, industrial claims that EFM is too "costly" to implement amount to an assertion that societal benefits from the forest industry are so great that they justify precedence over ecological objectives.

One way to evaluate the importance of the forest industry to society is to tally the revenue it generates for the province. In fiscal year 2001, revenue to the Government of Alberta, in the form of timber royalties and fees, was $72.9 million (AE, 2001: 47). An additional $303 million was received in the form of corporate income tax and property tax, for a total return of $376 million (AFPA, 2001). This amounts to 1.8% of the total provincial revenue in 2001 of $21.2 billion (GOA, 2002). But the province also incurs costs in maintaining the forest industry. These costs relate to harvest planning for quota holders, regulatory approvals, compliance monitoring, policy development, fire protection, fish and wildlife management, construction and maintenance of highways and grid roads, and a range of other items. At various times the province has also absorbed millions of dollars in loan defaults by forestry companies. A breakdown of the cost of these various activities is unavailable, but total expenditures for Alberta Environment in 2001 (which also had partial administrative responsibility for the petroleum sector) were $361 million (AE, 2001: 47). The implication is that the forestry sector's impact on the provincial economy is minor, and possibly negligible once all costs are figured in.

Another measure of the societal benefit of the forest industry is employment. According to Pratt and Urquhart (1994: 15) employment, not rent collection, may in fact have been the government's primary policy objective in its expansion of the forest industry. However, the decision to expand the industry through large, technologically advanced pulp and paper mills, at the expense of labour-intensive local mills, meant that only about 4100 jobs were added as result of the expansion in the late 1980s (Pratt and Urquhart, 1994: 7). In 2000, total direct employment in the primary forestry sector (including logging, lumber mills, pulp and paper, and panelboard) was 11,352 (AFPA, 2001). This amounts to 0.7% of the 1,627,300 Albertans employed in 2002 (AHRE, 2002). The implication is that the forestry sector is of very minor importance as a source of employment. In fact, more individuals are directly employed in the operation of parks than in the forestry sector, despite the large disparity in the land base of the two sectors (Dobson and Thompson, 1996) (Fig. 9.2).

In conclusion, societal benefits from the forest industry are relatively minor in Alberta. It should be possible to implement EFM without any noticeable economic repercussions at the provincial level. Certainly, reform of the tenure system, reallocation of timber, and implementation of new operating practices will be disruptive for many forestry companies in the short-term, to a greater or lesser degree. But in the long-term the new system promises increased stability. In particular, by maintaining old-growth on the landscape and reducing the rate of softwood harvest to a level that is sustainable over the long term, the new system will prevent a serious shortfall in softwood timber and a reduction in log size in future decades. Given that the wood manufactur-

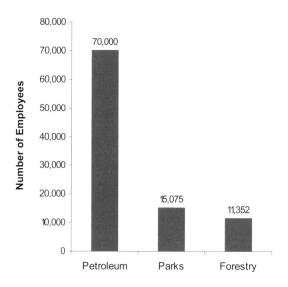

Fig. 9.2. Direct employment in major industrial sectors in Alberta. Sources: Petroleum (2001) = SC, 2002; Parks (1994) = Dobson and Thompson, 1996; Forestry (2000) = AFPA, 2001.

ing sector (cabinets, furniture, flooring, etc.) accounts for even more jobs than the primary forest sector (AFPA, 2001), stability in the supply of high-quality softwood logs is especially important. A transition to EFM will also mean that companies in Alberta will not be denied access to markets once forest certification becomes prevalent.

Petroleum Sector

In contrast to the forest industry, there can be no doubt that the petroleum industry is vital to Alberta's economy (Fig. 9.3). However, this does not imply that the existing system is the best one, or that controls on landscape-level impacts of the petroleum sector are inappropriate. Again, it is a matter of balancing economic and ecological objectives.

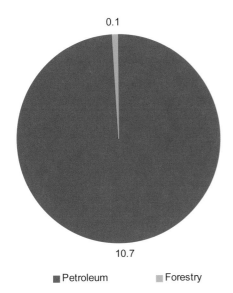

0.1

10.7

■ Petroleum   ■ Forestry

Fig. 9.3. Revenue ($ billions) of the petroleum sector and forestry sector in Alberta in 2001. Sources: Petroleum = ARD, 2001; Forestry = AE, 2001.

The first point to be made is that many practices designed to reduce the ecological footprint of the petroleum sector will actually result in cost savings for the industry. A case in point is the integration of road construction between the petroleum industry and the forest industry. A pilot study involving the 500 km² Gulf Surmont project southeast of Fort McMurray demonstrated that integrated planning with Al-Pac would result in a 50% decrease in road construction, relative to conventional planning, and a cost saving of approximately $1.1 million (Pope, 2001). Seismic programs are another area where ecological and economic benefits could both be realized. Once new enviro-drills become widely available it should be possible to cut narrow seismic lines with less effort, and cost, than the 5-7m wide lines that are cut today using bulldozers. Moreover, petroleum companies will save mil-

lions of dollars per year in reduced timber damage fees paid to forestry companies and may gain additional millions in the form of carbon credits.

Another point of consideration is that the rapid pace of petroleum development in Alberta is largely predicated on a system of low economic rents. According to a recent study by the Parkland Institute, this system is costing Albertans billions of dollars a year in foregone royalties and taxes (Macnab et al., 1999: 9). Meanwhile, excessive growth of the petroleum industry is causing social disruption in northeast Alberta (Parkinson, 2001) and enormous environmental degradation. By raising royalty rates, the pace of petroleum development could be moderated to a more appropriate level, without a significant decline in revenue flow. Furthermore, this approach would maximize the value of non-renewable petroleum resources to Albertans. Other comparable jurisdictions, such as Alaska and Norway, have successfully employed a strategy of high rents while maintaining a prosperous petroleum industry and building petroleum savings funds substantially larger than Alberta's (Fig. 9.4).

A Time for Change

Although the boreal forest presents a seemingly endless expanse, it does in fact have limits, and they are now being reached. The days of the open frontier are over, and the attitude that the forest can be all things to all interests is no longer tenable, if indeed it ever was. The time for change has come.

Many of the prerequisites for changing course are already in hand. The AFCS supplies the consensus vision and goals and a set of fundamental principles that are to guide forest management in

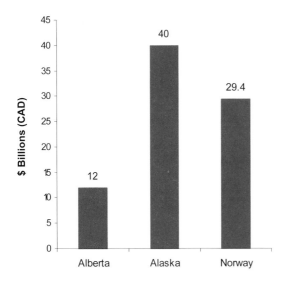

Fig. 9.4. Size of petroleum savings fund in Alberta (Heritage Fund), Alaska (Permanent Fund), and Norway (Petroleum Fund) in 1997. Source: Macnab et al., 1999.

the future. EFM provides the conceptual framework for achieving these new goals. Finally, the scientific and legal communities in Alberta, together with a few progressive forestry companies, have been working to develop policies and practices for putting the concepts of EFM into practice. The next step is wide-scale implementation.

Implementation involves organizational restructuring, the development of integrated management plans, and reform of legislation, regulations, and practices. The government's establishment of the Division of Integration Resource Management and its initiation of an integrated management planning process represent important steps in this direction. The next and most crucial step is to undertake the fundamental legal and regulatory reforms required to bring the process to a successful conclusion.

Unfortunately, there is no indication that the government is prepared to undertake anything but incremental change. In the five years since the AFCS was released it has been industry (i.e., a few progressive forestry companies), not government, that has shown leadership and made demonstrable progress in implementing EFM. Government action has been largely limited to policy pronouncements and the initiation of additional consultative exercises. Most troubling is the fact that the new consultative processes fail to include the AFCS as a starting point! On the ground, forests continue to be allocated on the basis of sustained-yield management; antiquated operating ground rules remain in effect; cumulative industrial impacts remain unregulated; companies continue to plan their operations independently; and the entire process is still governed by 1950s-era legislation. Furthermore, the political power base continues to reside in the departments of Energy and Sustainable Resource Management, not in the Division of Integrated Resource Management, suggesting that the political will to effect major reforms is lacking.

The government's reluctance to engage in meaningful and timely reform is remarkable on several counts. First, the AFCS represents a consensus that included the Alberta Forest Products Association and the Canadian Association of Petroleum Producers as signatories. Second, a large majority of Albertans, the ultimate owners of the resource, desire protection of the forest over development (Fig. 9.5). Finally, EFM is recognized by the scientific and management community as the state-of-the-art in forest management, while sustained-yield management has effectively been discredited.

The government's aversion to forestry reform can perhaps best be understood through comparison with other jurisdictions. As it turns out, initial reluctance to embrace EFM, or any major

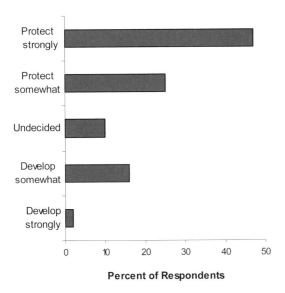

Fig. 9.5. Response of prairie province residents to the question: Is it more important to DEVELOP the boreal forest as an economic resource OR is it more important to PROTECT it in its natural state? Source: MacAllister Opinion Research, Sept. 2001 poll for Canadian Boreal Trust.

change for that matter, is not uncommon. Political scientist Jeremy Wilson, in his analysis of 30 years of forestry policy in British Columbia, provides insight into why this may be so (Wilson, 1998: 334):

Governments the world over muddle through. They try to plan, but mostly they react. They spend a fair bit of time grappling with states of full or partial paralysis brought on by uncertainty, inadequate information and capacity, internal divisions, and conflicting advice or pressures. For the most part they move incrementally. Overwhelmed by the complexity of problems they confront, decision-makers lean heavily on preexisting policy frameworks, adjusting only at the margins to accommodate distinctive features of new situations. Occasionally, when the planets are aligned, governments seize the opportunity to

consolidate disparate policy tendencies into a coherent shift in policy direction.

Our government's reluctance to follow through with the reforms dictated by the AFCS may, therefore, amount to simple inertia. After more than 30 years in power, the Progressive Conservative party may simply be an old dog disinclined to learn new tricks. More specifically, having built a party platform rooted in economic development, it may be incapable of recognizing workable solutions that do not involve maximizing the rate of industrial profits. These basic tendencies are undoubtedly influenced and reinforced by strong industrial lobbies.

Despite the government's unwillingness to champion EFM, there is yet hope for our forest. The basis for this hope lies in another of Wilson's observations (Wilson, 1998: 343): "*Policy making is mostly about expediting or delaying the way immutable forces unfold, or about nudging the resultant change trajectories a few degrees to one side or another.*" The public's desire for ecological management is one of these immutable forces, and the ultimate implementation of EFM in Alberta is inevitable. It happened in the Pacific Northwest of the United States. It happened in British Columbia. It happened in Ontario. Eventually, it will happen in Alberta. The question is, how long will it take?

Until now the government has been able to successfully employ delay tactics based on re-labelling old ideas with new terminology and symbol-laden policy statements that are devoid of measurable objectives. But these tactics are effective for only a limited time. By adopting the language of EFM, the government becomes bound by the tests and standards of that model. Moreover, the capacity of external organizations to as-

149

sess the government's performance against these tests and standards is rapidly increasing. Unless meaningful reforms are undertaken, the government's position will become progressively indefensible and untenable.

In a democratic system such as ours, indefensible policies and indifference to the broad public interest cannot be maintained indefinitely. Eventually, our leaders will be compelled to exert the political will necessary to see through the required reform of forest management. But time is of the essence. Every additional year of delay forecloses options and further diminishes the integrity of the forest. Therefore, it is incumbent on all Albertans who value the forest for the many benefits it provides, who abhor the idea that caribou and other species may become extinct, and who are concerned about the legacy we are leaving for our children, to make their voices heard.

Literature Cited

AE (Alberta Environment). 2001. Annual report 2000/2001. Alberta Environment, Edmonton, AB. (Available at: www.gov.ab.ca/env/dept/).

AE (Alberta Environment). 2002. Sustainable resource and environmental management prototype project. Alberta Environment, Edmonton, AB. (Available at: http://www3.gov.ab.ca/env/regions/nes/prototype.html)

AFCSSC (Alberta Forest Conservation Strategy Steering Committee). 1997. Alberta forest conservation strategy. Alberta Environmental Protection, Edmonton, AB. (Available at: www.borealcentre.ca/reports/reports.html)

AFMSC (Alberta Forest Management Science Council). 1997. Sustainable forest management and its major elements. Report prepared for Alberta Environmental Protection, Edmonton, AB. (Available at: www.borealcentre.ca/reports/reports.html)

AFPA (Alberta Forest Products Association). 2001. Alberta forest products industry: overview and economic impact. Alberta Forest Products Association, Edmonton, AB.

AHRE (Alberta Human Resources and Employment).

2002. Labour force statistics. Alberta Human Resources and Employment, Edmonton, AB. (Available at: www3.gov.ab.ca/hre/lfstats.htm)

ARD (Alberta Resource Development). 2001. Annual report: 2000/2001. Alberta Resource Development, Edmonton, AB. (Available at: www.energy.gov.ab.ca)

Cumming, S. and G. Armstrong. 1999. Divided land bases and overlapping tenures in Alberta's boreal forests: a simulation study of policy alternatives. SFM Working Paper 1999-3. Sustainable Forest Management Network, Edmonton, AB. (Available at: http://sfm-1.biology.ualberta.ca/english/home/index.htm)

Dobson, S. and J. Thompson. 1996. Parks and protected areas: their contribution to the Alberta economy. Alberta Environmental Protection, Edmonton, AB.

Euler, D. and E. Epp. 2000. A new foundation for Ontario forest policy for the 21st century. Pages 276-294 in Perera, A., D. Euler, and I. D. Thompson, editors. Ecology of a managed terrestrial landscape. Ontario Ministry of Natural Resources, Toronto, ON.

GOA (Government of Alberta). 2002. The right decisions for challenging times: Alberta budget 2002. Government of Alberta, Edmonton, AB. (Available at: www.finance.gov.ab.ca/business/budget/index.html)

GOO (Government of Ontario). 1994. Crown Forest Sustainability Act. Queen's Printer for Ontario, Toronto, ON. (Available at: www.gov.on.ca/MBS/english/common/queens.html)

Kennett, S.A. 2002. Integrated resource management in Alberta: past, present and benchmarks for the future. Canadian Institute of Resources Law, Calgary, AB.

Lieffers, V., R. Macmillan, D. MacPherson, K. Branter, and J. Stewart. 1996. Semi-natural and intensive silvicultural systems for the boreal mixedwood forest. For. Chron. 72:286-292.

Macnab, B., J. Daniels, and G. Laxer. 1999. Giving away the Alberta advantage. Are Albertans receiving maximum revenues from their oil and gas? Parkland Institute, Edmonton, AB.

MOR (McAllister Opinion Research). 2001. Poll commissioned for the Canadian Boreal Trust, September, 2001.

OFAAB (Ontario Forest Accord Advisory Board). 2001. State of the Ontario Forest Accord. Ontario Ministry of Natural Resources, Toronto, ON. (Available at: www.mnr.gov.on.ca)

Parkinson, D. 2001. Fort McMurray suffers growing pains. Globe and Mail, October 1, 2001 – Page B1.

Pope, D. 2001. Integrated landscape management on the Alpac FMA. In: Oil and gas planning on forested lands in Alberta: overview of CIF-RMS technical session, March 23, 2001. Canadian Institute of Forestry, Edmonton, AB.

Pratt, L. and I. Urquhart. 1994. The last great forest. NeWest Press, Edmonton, AB.

Ross, M. 2001. Legal and institutional responses to conflicts involving the oil and gas and forestry sectors. Canadian Institute of Resources Law, Calgary, AB.

SC (Statistics Canada). 2002. Query of CANSIM II database: Table 281-0024 - Employment (SEPH) by type of employee for selected industries classified using the North American Industry Classification System (NAICS). Statistics Canada, Ottawa, ON. (Available at: http://cansim2.statcan.ca)

Schieck, J. and S. J. Song. 2002. Responses of boreal birds to wildfire and harvesting. Pages 9-1 to 9-45 in Song, S. J., editor. Ecological basis for stand management: a synthesis of ecological responses to wildfire and harvesting. Alberta Research Council, Vegreville, AB.

Sinton, H. 2001. Prairie oil and gas: a lighter footprint. Alberta Environment, Edmonton, AB.

Song, S. J. 2002. Ecological basis for stand management: a synthesis of ecological responses to wildfire and harvesting. Alberta Research Council, Vegreville, AB.

Walters, C. 1997. Adaptive policy design: thinking at large spatial scales. In Bissonette, J. A., editor. Wildlife and landscape ecology: effects of pattern and scale. Springer , New York.

Wilson, J. 1998. Talk and log: wilderness politics in British Columbia. UBC Press, Vancouver, B.C.

Glossary

Cohort: A group of trees (or other entities) of similar origin, and hence of the same age.

Ecological integrity: The degree to which all ecosystem components and their interactions are represented and functioning.

Ecosystem: An assemblage of populations of plants, animals, bacteria, and fungi, together with their environment, treated together as a functional unit..

Edge: The transition between two distinct patch types. In the text I primarily focus on the edge between human-caused features and intact forest.

Landscape: I use the term landscape to denote areas of a few hundred to a few thousand hectares (i.e., larger than a stand, but smaller than a region).

Mixedwood forest: Forest stands comprised of both hardwoods and softwoods. Mixedwood stands containing aspen and white spruce typify upland sites in Alberta's boreal forest.

Monoculture: Growth of a single species, such as white spruce, through artificial planting and the suppression of competing vegetation.

Natural Disturbance Model: An approach to forest harvesting that sets targets for forest structures and patterns based on the emulation of natural disturbance and renewal processes.

Patch: A group of contiguous stands that are of similar age and type (e.g., old-growth aspen).

Phase 3 inventory: A non-spatial forest inventory of the province completed in 1984 by the Alberta government. Based on aerial photography.

Region: I use the term region to denote areas of a few hundred square kilometers to many thousands of square kilometers (i.e., larger than landscapes). In most cases in the text I equate the regional scale with Natural Subregions.

Riparian zones: The forest adjacent to natural water courses.

Scale: Refers to the size (or type) of units within which observations are made. In the text I use three spatial scales: forest stands, landscapes, and regions.

Senescence: Deterioration and death associated with advanced age.

Snag: A standing dead tree from which the top has broken off.

Species richness: Refers to the number of species in a study area; one measure of biodiversity.

Stand: A group of trees that share a defined set of attributes (e.g., 80-year old, B-density aspen). Designation of stands is usually done through the interpretation of aerial photographs, focusing on the dominant tree species. Most stands are initiated through disturbance events such as fire.

Succession: Process of stand development over time involving tree maturation and death and changes in species composition. The predictable patterns of change, which are unique for each stand type, are referred to as successional trajectories or paths.

Sustained-yield management: Approach that seeks to achieve a sustained flow of timber from the forest, without explicit requirements for the maintenance of biodiversity or ecological function.

Understory: Plant life that exists beneath the canopy of large mature trees in a forest stand.